CW00385818

About the author

W.J. Dempster is a retired surgeon who has a long-standing interest in Darwin's life and, as it were, the 'origin of the *Origin*'. He is the author of *An Introduction to Experimental Surgery Studies* (Blackwell) and *Patrick Matthew and Natural Selection* (Pentland Press). He currently resides in Hampshire, England.

First published in Great Britain in 2005 by
The Book Guild Ltd
25 High Street
Lewes, East Sussex
BN7 2LU

Typesetting in Times by
Keyboard Services, Luton, Bedfordshire

Printed in Great Britain by
Athenaeum Press Ltd, Gateshead

A catalogue record for this book is available from the
British Library

ISBN 1 85776 907 4

CONTENTS

ACKNOWLEDGEMENTS

I have had immense help from my dear wife.

I thank The Book Guild for their cooperation and courage in publishing a book with a more balanced appreciation of Charles Darwin.

The portrait of John Hunter was reproduced by the kind permission of The President and Council of The Royal College of Surgeons of England.

Tina Craig, deputy librarian of The Royal College of Surgeons of England, kindly provided photocopies of some pages from *Essays and Observations* 1861.

I have been greatly assisted by Joanna Bentley and Janet Wrench in preparing the text.

in disgust. Smith's verdict on Balliol was this: 'one of the learned societies that have chosen to remain for a very long time, the sanctuaries in which exploded systems and obsolete prejudices found shelter and protection after they had been hunted out of every other corner of the world' (Ross 1996).

Years later, in 1787, Smith visited London for the last time. He was in rather an emaciated condition and went to John Hunter for help. He was cut successfully for piles and then made a slow recovery. During a previous visit to London in 1773 he attended William Hunter's anatomy lectures.

Edward Gibbon attended Magdalen College between 1752 and 1753, and found the teaching boring. He too left, having spent 'fourteen unprofitable months' there (Ross 1996). Jeremy Bentham attended Oxford in 1761. Being made to subscribe to the 39 articles of the Church of England made him develop radical views and a hostility to established institutions. So, it is no wonder that John Hunter walked out after two months, bent on educating himself.

Critics of Hunter were usually those who knew little of his work. A critic in this mode was Trotter. In his Oration of 1932 he had this to say:

It is impossible, however, not to be struck by a certain disproportion between the amount of energy and genius that was expended and the harvest of substantial knowledge that was gathered. Many of the researches were indecisive, not a few of the conclusions were incorrect, and no single advance was won which could be said to mark an epoch in the history of knowledge ... few can be equally convinced that he made a direct contribution to the science of the day fully commensurate with his splendid gifts.

How can a man with 'splendid gifts' (whatever that means), energy and genius produce nothing of importance?

Richard Owen studied all Hunter's work and made the following assessments:

the proper aim of geological investigation, and the right way of investigating, and the true extent of investigation, are, at the outset, recognised and defined by Hunter.

(on *Essays and Observations*)

The present part of the Hunterian Collection plainly shows that Hunter duly appreciated the study of fossil remains both as extending the knowledge of the modifications of animal structure, and as throwing light on the past history and changes of the earth.

(on *Reptilia & Pisces*, 1834)

Some idea may be formed of Hunter's extraordinary diligence by the fact that his museum contained at the time of his death upwards of 10,000 preparations illustrative of human and comparative anatomy, physiology and pathology, and natural history.

(Weld's *History of the Royal Society*, 1848)

Although the scientific climate had changed a great deal since 1790, Richard Owen introduced Hunter's works with more than a hint that Council members were apprehensive; '...some may wish that the world had never known that Hunter thought so differently on some subjects from what they believed, and would have desired him to think'. That the scientific and social climates had changed is indicated by Owen's scornful reference to the Noachian mythology:

I need not trespass on your time by recounting the hundred-fold additional and diversified testimony, which God, in his wisdom, has suffered to be made manifest ... in demonstrating the utter inadequacy of any of the brief and transient traditional deluges to account for observed geological and palaeontological phenomena...

By the time that Owen came to lecture on Hunter's essays in 1855, ecology had made great strides, palaeontology was growing fast and ichthyology, pure Hunterian observation, was well established. Owen pays glowing tribute to the prescience of Hunter in all these basic subjects. It was characteristic of Hunter to occupy himself with theory and experiment and constant revision, and he had, by 1790, set out the dynamic laws of geology regarding the effect of running water, the deposition of matter transported by water, the erosive action of the sea, the effect of volcanic eruptions and the deposits from animal and vegetable matter. Both Hunter and Hutton (in 1778) recognised that geology was concerned with changes on the surface of the earth and both attempted to explain the past in terms of the present. But Hutton (in 1793) had nothing to say about fossils. By 1855 Owen could claim that Hunter's geological observations on the Thames Valley and Alentejo had been confirmed.

So why no apotheosis? There can be no avoiding the conclusion that it was due to the timidity, the jealousy and the ignorance of the Fellows of the College of Surgeons, supported, of course, by Hunter's refusal during his lifetime to work within the accepted centres of erudition at Oxbridge. Such centres, with all their classical pretentiousness, stereotyped expressions and blatant religiosity, could be relied upon to squeeze Hunter off the stage of scientific fame, as was the fate of Edward Blyth (Eiseley 1959).

Of the Thames Valley, Hunter wrote some years prior to 1790, when orthodox views on the Mosaic dogma were held by everyone including fellows of the Royal Society:

> Probably the whole flat tract of the River Thames, between its lateral hills, was an arm of the sea, and as the German Ocean became shallower, it was gradually reduced to a river; and the composition of this tract of land, for an immense depth, would show it as a gravel, a sand and a clay, with fossil shells in the clay 200 or 300 feet deep, all deposited when it was an arm of the sea, and above which are found bones of land animals, where it has been shallow.
>
> (*Observations on Geology*, 1859)

This betrayed a view of nature too pagan in its implications for the society Hunter lived in and condemned him to an eternity of punishment.

Hunter was a philosopher who had his papers burned, his unpublished observations plagiarised or suppressed, his specimens sold, lost or bombed, his radicalism embalmed and his character maligned, his sudden death unrecorded by his hospital colleagues and the broad canvas of his life's work torn to shreds by Hunterian orators. Such was the fate of one of the greatest natural philosophers science has ever known.

Buckle introduced Hunter as a man 'whose only fault was an occasional obscurity, not merely of language but also of thought'. He then goes on to compare Hunter with Adam Smith, whose clarity of thought was superior because he had stuck to the deduction of ideas: 'With Hunter, on the contrary, it sometimes seemed as if the understanding was troubled by the grandeur of its own conceptions, and doubted what path it had to take'. Frankly, I don't understand what Buckle is trying to convey here.

When Darwin was writing the *Origin of Species* he used to send parts to Joseph Hooker for comments. Hooker informed Darwin that he found many passages 'obscure', and Darwin replied, 'Thank you for telling me about obscurity of style. But on my life no man with lash over him could have worked harder at clearness than I have'. Hunter and Darwin were working at the cutting edge of subjects and perhaps for this reason tended to be obscure.

It seems that the critics of Hunter were not his pupils. Here is one Mr Otley: 'In his writings we occasionally find an obscurity in the expression of his thoughts, a want of logical accuracy in his reasonings, and an incorrectness in his language resulting from a deficient education.' In his autobiography, Darwin admitted that he had made little of Latin and Greek and had learned nothing at school. So, he had a deficient education as well.

Hunter's former pupils had a different story to relate. Here is his devoted pupil, Abernethy: 'he appears to me as a new character in our profession; and, briefly to express his primary merit, I may call him the first and greatest physionosologist or expositor of the nature of disease' (Oration, 1819).

Sir Benjamin Brodie's tribute to Hunter also says much:

It is true that the essential parts of John Hunter's doctrines as to inflammation and its consequences are now so incorporated with what is taught in the schools, that to be acquainted with them you need not seek them in his works; but I recommend you, nevertheless, to make these your especial study, for the sake of the other valuable information which they contain, and the important views in physiology and pathology which, in almost every page, are offered to your contemplation.

In 1835, a Mr Palmer wrote: 'Those who have traced the progress of modern surgery to its trace source, will not fail to have discerned, in the principles Hunter established, the germs of almost all the improvements which have been since introduced'. Buckle had seemingly forgotten about Hunter's 'obscurity' when he observed:

an essay on geology. There is evidence that during this period, Hunter was suffering from angina, but his post-mortem showed no sign of syphilis. No one suggested that Hunter had suffered from cerebral syphilis during his lifetime, and there is no record of anyone remarking that Hunter had at any time displayed blotched skin or smelled of mercury ointment. Hunter's numerous students would be daily in close contact with him and yet not one appears to have noticed anything untoward. Above all, Hunter's wife and brother were not aware of the alleged condition.

Despite this, in 1835 a Mr G.G. Babington, editor of *The Surgical Works of John Hunter*, inserted a footnote – only a footnote – stating that 'the author [John Hunter] inoculated himself with the matter of gonorrhoea, and the consequence was the production of chancres, followed by bubo, and secondary symptoms'. A mere footnote with no evidence to support seems to be the sole cause of this slur on Hunter's honour.

I must say that the 1767 experiment in Hunter's book does not make sense. It is in contradiction with the rest of the book. Hunter knew very well that mercury could not cure syphilis, so I am at a loss to explain why he should have written such a nonsensical statement. Furthermore, between 1764 and 1771 Hunter was courting the daughter of an army surgeon he had become friendly with during the campaign of 1761–3. They married in 1771. Is it likely that Hunter would visit the woman he wished to marry smelling of mercury and exhibiting blotched skin, with an ulcer, a bubo and chancre of the penis? This is beyond belief. The allegation should be disowned by the College of Surgeons.

Another allegation, this time by Livesley and Pentelow (1978), is that Hunter did not inoculate *himself* but rather his 12-year-old brother-in-law, Everard Home. This makes Hunter a child abuser and criminal! This too seems impossible. Everard was at that time attending Westminster School. Is it credible that a boy could attend school with blotched skin and all the other symptoms and no one would notice? The authors of this allegation thank 'Miss Jessie Dobson' for 'constructive comments'. They postulate that Everard, now an old man, was looking for the original statement of the 1767 incident. If he was looking for this document, why burn a mass of Hunter's unpublished essays? In any case, once Hunter's works were published the original was used to light the candles!

In 1781, Erasmus Darwin married for the second time and took his bride to London for six weeks. The highlight of his visit was attending the discussion group at the New Slaughter's Coffee House in St Martin's Lane, presided over by John Hunter. Erasmus had met John when he attended William Hunter's anatomy lectures in 1853. John was now a distinguished surgeon and well integrated in London's social scene. It is more than likely that Erasmus would have been invited to John's house in Leicester Square. They were both interested in similar subjects and so would have had interesting exchanges. There is no evidence that Erasmus contacted John Hunter after this visit and there are no letters like the correspondence Erasmus carried on with Joseph Banks, the President of the Royal Society. So many of Hunter's unpublished papers were destroyed that it is impossible to trace what Erasmus gained from his visit. He knew sometime earlier that John Hunter had several copies of Buffon's *Histoire Naturelle*. In a letter to Watt, dated 29 March 1775, Erasmus says that Hunter had 27 volumes of the *Histoire*. How would Erasmus have known this unless he had made contact with Hunter before his honeymoon visit to London in 1871?

These two were polymaths. Erasmus was a great inventor and few subjects escaped his enquiring mind – medicine, geology, chemistry, zoology and, above all, botany. From that delirium of intellectual activity developed a belief that humans had evolved from lower forms, so anticipating Lamarck.

Erasmus' last years, like Hunter's, were tinged by sadness. All his old friends had died. The support for the French Revolution of 1789 by members of the Lunar Society led to its demise. The tragic death of his son affected him profoundly. His poetry, which had been so highly praised, was now out of favour and severely criticised by Wordsworth and Coleridge, although they were both influenced by him.

In England in the eighteenth century, human freaks were regularly exhibited at fairs and were popular exhibits. John Hunter acquired a collection of 'monsters', both human and animal. It is clear from Darwin's notebooks, particularly notebook D, that he paid a great deal of attention to Hunter's essays on this subject and grouped various remarks into what he referred to as 'Hunter's Law'. This is part of what Hunter wrote:

Every deviation from that original form and structure which gives the distinguishing character to the productions of Nature, may not be improperly called monstrous. According to the

36

acceptance of this term, the variety of monsters will be almost infinite; and, as far as my knowledge has extended, there is not a species of animal, nay, there is not a single part of an animal body, which is not subject to an extraordinary formation. Neither does this appear to be a matter of chance, for it may be observed that every species has a disposition to deviate from Nature in a manner peculiar to itself. It is likewise worth of remark, that each species of animal is disposed to have nearly the same sort of defects, and to have certain supernumerary parts of the same kind; yet every part is not alike disposed to take on a great variety of forms; but each part of each species seems to have its monstrous form originally impressed upon it.

This is why Hunter considered the cause of congenital malformation as existing in the primordial germ. Geoffroy St Hilaire considered that monstrosities were due to external causes at some point during foetal development. Hunter has proved to be correct. We know now that there are genes that control the development of the body. To produce 'monsters', biologists now have only to alter a single gene, either by shutting it down or changing the time or place where it makes its protein. There is an entire family of related genes, called 'hox' genes, which do the same job in all animals so far investigated, and so can be transplanted from one animal to another.

On the *Origin of Species*

Does not the natural gradation of animals, from one to another, lead to the original species? And does not that mode of investigation gradually lead to the knowledge of that species? Are we not led on to the wolf by the gradual affinity of the different varieties in the dog? Could we not trace out the gradation in the cat, horse, cow, sheep, fowl, etc. in a like manner?

It would appear that Darwin took from this page of Hunter's manuscript the title of his famous book, *On Origin of Species by Means of Natural Selection*. This passage is taken from Volume 1, page 37 of *Essays and Observations*, edited by Owen and published in 1861. Darwin read Hunter's essays before they were published by Owen, and Owen probably directed Darwin's attention to Hunter's work at a time when he was identifying the fossils Darwin sent home from the *Beagle*.

Hunter had wondered why fossils were being found in an area where they could no longer live in the present climate. His acute mind and his economy of effort led him to suspect that, during the past history of the earth, the climate had repeatedly changed. The cause of these changes might be shifts in the sun's annual path through the fixed stars. This is what Hunter wrote:

> as the sea must have at some period overflowed the now land, this gives us a hint of the variation that must have taken place in the centre of gravity of the earth, and also as the fossils now found in countries who's climate does not correspond with the climates now inhabited by the recent [Holocene today] we are led to suppose that there has been an alteration in the ecliptic [of the sun].

It was not until the second half of the nineteenth century that John Croll (1801–90) came to suspect that the changes in the earth's orbit round the sun rather than the ecliptic, as Hunter had suggested, were responsible for the ice ages. This was now a mathematical problem. Croll calculated the changes in the earth's orbit, now referred to as the eccentricities of orbit, over the last 3 million years. This was the first time that a geologist had done this. Croll found that the eccentricity of the orbit changed cyclically – high and low eccentricities. We are now in a low eccentricity. Now, thanks to Croll we know how the sun's radiation is distributed over the planetary surfaces – the eccentricity of the orbit, the tilt of the axis of rotation and the position of the equinoxes in the precessional cycle. Croll was elected a Fellow of the Royal Society in 1876 and he is yet another example of a self-educated man. Imbrie and Imbrie (1979) In the twentieth century it was discovered that the crust of the earth rested on tectonic plates that moved by convection and could account for the migration of England from the equator to its present position.

2

Patrick Matthew and the Process of Natural Selection

It is perhaps not always recognised how complete the anticipation really was.

(Calman 1912)

Patrick Matthew

In the 1872 *Historical Sketch*, prefixed to the sixth edition of the *Origin of Species*, Charles Darwin made this statement concerning Patrick Matthew:

In 1831 Mr Patrick Matthew published his work on *Naval Timber and Arboriculture*, in which he gives precisely the same view on the origin of species as that (presently to be alluded to) propounded by Mr Wallace and myself in the *Linnean Journal*, and as that enlarged in the present volume. Unfortunately the view was given by Mr Matthew very briefly in scattered passages in an Appendix to a work on a different subject, so that it remained unnoticed until Mr Matthew himself drew attention to it in the *Gardeners' Chronicle* on April 7th, 1860. The differences of Mr Matthew's view from mine are not of much importance: he seems to consider that the world was nearly depopulated at successive periods, and then restocked; and he gives as an alternative, that new forms may be generated 'without the presence of any mould or germ of former aggregates'. I am not sure that I understand some passages; but it seems that he attributes much influence to the direct action of the conditions of life. He clearly saw, however, the full force of the principle of natural selection.

And here is the text of Matthew's Appendix:

Note A
It is only on the Ocean that Universal Empire is practicable – only by means of Navigation that all the world can be subdued or retained under One dominion. On land, the greatest numbers, and quantity of materiel, are unavailable, excepting around the spot where they are produced. The most powerful army is crippled by advancing a few degrees in an enemy's territory, unless when aided by some catching enthusiasm; its resources get distant, communication is obstructed – subjection does not extend beyond the range of its guns, and it quickly melts away. The impossibility of dominion extending over a great space, when communication is only by land, has often been proved. The rule of Cyrus, or Alexander, the Caesars, the Tartar conquerors, or Bonaparte, did not extend over a tithe of the earth; and we may believe that, by some of these chiefs, dominion was extended as widely as under land communication could be effected – further than it could be supported.

On the contrary, when a powerful nation has her war-like strength afloat, and possesses naval superiority, independent of being unassailable herself, every spot of the world, wherever a wave can roll, is accessible to her power and under her control. In a very short time she can throw an irresistible force, unexhausted by marches, and with every resource, upon any hostile point, the point of attack being in her own choice, and unknown to the enemy. In case of her dependent dominions being scattered over the two hemispheres, her means of communication, and consequent power of defending these and supporting authority, are more facile than what exists between the seat of government of any ordinary-sized continental kingdom and its provinces. Were a popular system of colonial government adopted, many islands and inferior states would find it their interest to become incorporated as part of the Empire.

Note B

There is a law universal in nature, tending to render every reproductive being the best possibly suited to its condition that its kind, or that organised matter, is susceptible of, which appears intended to model the physical and mental or instinctive powers, to their highest perfection, and to continue them so. This law sustains the lion in his strength, the hare in her swiftness, and the fox in his wiles. As Nature, in all her modifications of life, has a power of increase far beyond what is needed to supply the place of what falls by Time's decay, those individuals who possess not the requisite strength, swiftness, hardihood, or cunning, fall prematurely without reproducing – either a prey to their natural devourers, or sinking under disease, generally induced by want of nourishment, their place being occupied by the more perfect of their own kind, who are pressing on the means of subsistence. The law of entail, necessary to hereditary nobility, is an outrage on this law of Nature which She will not pass unavenged – a law which has the most debasing influence upon the energies of a people, and will sooner or later lead to general subversion, more especially when the executive of a country remains for a considerable time efficient, and no effort is needed on the part of the nobility to protect their own, or no war to draw forth or preserve their powers by exertion. It is all very well, when, in stormy times, the baron has every faculty trained to its utmost ability in keeping his proud crest aloft. How far hereditary nobility, under effective government, has operated to retard 'the march of intellect', and deteriorate the species in modern Europe, is an interesting and important question. We have seen it play its part in France; we see exhibition of its influence throughout the Iberian peninsula, to the utmost degradation of its victims. It has rendered the Italian peninsula, with its islands, a blank in the political map of Europe. Let the panegyrists of hereditary nobility, primogeniture, and entail, say what these countries might not have been but for the baneful influence of this unnatural custom. It is an eastern proverb, that no king is many removes from a shepherd. Most conquerors and founders of dynasties have followed the plough or the flock. Nobility, to be in the highest perfection, like the finer varieties of fruits, independent of having its vigour excited by regular married alliance with wilder stocks, would require stated complete renovation, by selection anew, from among the purest crab. In some places, this renovation would not be so soon requisite as in others, and, judging from facts, we would instance Britain as perhaps the soil where nobility will continue the longest untainted. As we advance nearer to the equator, renovation becomes sooner necessary, excepting at high elevation – in many places, every third generation, at least with the Caucasian breed, although the finest stocks be regularly imported. This renovation is required as well physically as morally.

It is chiefly in regard to the interval of time between the period of necessary feudal authority, and that when the body of the population [has] acquired the power of self-government.

From the spread of knowledge, claim a community of rights, that we have adverted to the use of war. The manufacturer, the merchant, the sailor, the capitalist, whose mind is not corrupted by the indolence induced under the law of entail, are too much occupied to require any stimulant beyond what the game in the wide field of commercial adventure affords. A great change in the circumstances of man is obviously at hand. In the first step beyond the condition of the wandering savage, while the lower classes from ignorance remained as helpless children, mankind naturally fell into clans under paternal or feudal government; but as children, when grown up to maturity, with the necessity for protection, lose the subordination to parental authority, so the great mass of the present population requiring no guidance from a particular class of feudal lords, will not continue to tolerate any hereditary claims of authority of one portion of the population over their fellow-men; nor any laws to keep up rank and wealth corresponding to this exclusive power. It would be wisdom in the noblesse of Europe to abolish every claim or law which serves to point them out a separate class, and, as quickly as possible, to merge themselves into the mass of the population. It is a law manifest in nature, that when the use of any thing is past, its existence is no longer kept up.

Although the necessity for the existence of feudal lords is past, yet the same does not hold in respect to a hereditary head or King; and the stability of this head of the government will, in no way, be lessened by such a change. In the present state of European society, perhaps no other rule can be so mild and efficient as that of a liberal benevolent monarch, assisted by a popular representative Parliament. The poorest man looks up to his King as his own, with affection and pride, and considers him a protector; while he only regards the antiquated feudal lord with contempt. The influence of a respected hereditary family, as head of a country, is also of great utility in forming a principle of union to the different members, and in giving unity and stability to the government.

In respect to our own great landholders themselves, we would ask, where is there that unnatural parent – that miserable victim of hereditary pride – who does not desire to see his domains equally divided among his own children? The high paid sinecures in Church and State will not much longer be a great motive for keeping up a powerful family head, whose influence may [burden] their fellow-citizens with the younger branches. Besides, when a portion of land is so large, that the owner cannot have an individual acquaintance and associations with every stream, and bush, and rock, and knoll, the deep enjoyment which the smaller native proprietor would have in the peculiar features, is not called forth, and is lost to man. The abolition of the law of entail and primogeniture, will, in the present state of civilisation, not only add to the happiness of the proprietor, heighten morality, and give much greater stability to the social order, but will also give a general stimulus to industry and improvement, increasing the comforts and elevating the condition of the operative class.

In the new state of things which is near at hand, the proprietor and the mercantile class will amalgamise – employment in useful occupations will not continue to be held in scorn – the merchant and manufacturer will no longer be barely tolerated to exist, harassed at every turn by imposts and the interference of petty tyrants; Government, instead of forming an engine of oppression, being simplified and based on morality and justice, will become a cheap and efficient protection to person and property; and the necessary taxation being levied from property alone, every individual will purchase in the cheapest market, and sell the produce of his industry in the dearest. This period might, perhaps, be accelerated throughout Europe, did the merchants and capitalists only know their own strength. Let them, as citizens of the world, hold annual congress in some central place, and deliberate on the interests of man, which is their own, and throw the whole of their influence to support liberal and just governments, and to repress slavery, crime, bigotry [and] tyranny in all shapes. A Rothschild might earn an unstained fame, as great as yet has been attained by man, by organising such a power, and presiding at its councils.

Note C
The influence of long continued impression, constituting instinct or habit of breed, is a curious phenomenon in the animal economy. Our population in the eastern maritime districts of Britain, descended principally from the Scandinavian rover, though devoted for a time to agricultural or mechanical occupation, betake themselves, when opportunity offers, to their old element, the ocean, and launch out upon the 'wintry wave' with much of the same home-felt composure as does the white polar bear. They roam over every sea and every shore, from Behring's Straits to Magellan's, with as little solicitude as the Kelt over his own misty hill, overcoming, in endurance, the native of the torrid zone under his vertical sun, and the native of the frigid among his polar snows.

To what may we ascribe the superiority of this portion of the Caucasian breed – may it arise in part from its repeated change of place under favourable circumstances? Other races have migrated, but not like this, always as conqueror. The Jew has been a stroller in his time; but he has improved more in mental acumen and cunning – not so much in heroism and personal qualities: his proscribed condition will account for this.

The habit of breed is apparent in many places of the world. Where a fine river washes the walls of some of the internal towns of France, scarce a boat is to be seen, except the long tract-boats employed in the conveyance of fire-wood – nobody thinks of sailing for pleasure. The Esquimaux, and the Red Indian of North America, inhabiting the same country, [show] an entirely distinct habit of breed. The Black and the Copper-coloured native[s] of the Australian lands, are equally opposed in instinctive habit.

The Caucasian in its progress, will also have mingled slightly, and, judging from analogy, perhaps advantageously, with the finer portion of those whom it has overwhelmed. This breed, by its wide move across the Atlantic, does not seem at all to have lost vigour, and retains the nautical and roving instinct unimpaired, although the American climate is certainly inferior to the European. It is there rapidly moving west, and may soon have described one of the earth's circles. A change of seed, that is, a change of place, within certain limits of latitude, is well known to be indispensable to the more sturdy growth and health of many cultivated vegetables; it is probable that this also holds true of the human race. There are few countries where the old breed has not again and again sunk before the vigour of new immigration; we even see the worn-out breed, chased from their homes to new location, return, after a time, superior to their former vanquishers, or gradually work their way back in peace, by superior subsisting power: this is visible in France, where the aboriginal sallow Kelt, distinguished by high satyr-like feature, deep-placed sparkling brown or grey eye, narrowed lower part of the face, short erect vertebral column, great mental acuteness, and restless vivacity, has emerged from the holes of the earth, the recesses of the forests and wastes, into which it had been swept before the more powerful blue-eyed Caucasian; and being a smaller, more easily subsisting animal, has, by starving and eating out, been gradually undermining the breed of its former conquerors. The changes which have been taking place in France, and which, in many places, leave now scarcely a trace of the fine race which existed twenty centuries ago, may, however, in part, be accounted for by the admixture of the Caucasian and Keltic tending more to the character of the latter, from the latter being a purer and more fixed variety, and nearer the original type or medium standard of man; and from the warm dry plains of France (much drier from cultivation and the reduction of the forests), having considerable influence to increase this bias: in some of the south-eastern departments, more immediately in the tide of the ingress of the Caucasian, where the purest current has latest flowed, and the climate is more suitable, and also in some of the maritime districts, where the air is moister, and to which they have been seaborn at a later period, the Caucasian character is still prominent. Something of this, yet not so general, is occurring in Britain, where the fair bright-blooded race is again giving place to the darker and more sallow. This may, however, be partly occasioned by more of artificial heat and shelter and other consequences of higher civilisation. There seems to be something connected with confinement and sedentary life, with morbid action of the liver, or respiratory or transpiratory organs, which tends to change under dry and hot, and especially confined atmosphere. Perhaps imagination is also at work and the colour most regarded, as snow in cold countries, black among colliers, white among bleachers, or even the dark colour of dress, may produce its peculiar impression, and our much looked-up-to Calvinistic priesthood, from the pulpit, disseminate darkness as well as light.

Our own Kelt has indubitably improved much since, *par necessite*, he took to the mountain; but, though steadily enduring, when there is mental excitement, he has acquired a distaste to dull hopeless unceasing labour, and would fare scantily and lie hard, rather than submit to the monotonous industry of the city operative, or the toil of the agricultural drudge. Though once a fugitive, the Kelt is now, in moral courage and hardihood, equal perhaps to any other, yet he still trembles to put foot on ocean.

Not withstanding that change of place, simply, may have impression to improve the species, yet is it more to circumstances connected with this change, to which the chief part of the improvement must be referred? In the agitation which accompanies emigration, the ablest in mind and body – the most powerful varieties of the race – will be thrown into their natural position as leaders, impressing the stamp of their character on the people at large, and constituting the more reproductive part; while the feebler or more improvident varieties will generally sink under the incidental hardships. When a swarm emigrates from a prosperous hive, it also will generally consist of the more adventurous stirring spirits, who, with the right of conquerors, will appropriate the finest of the indigenae which they overrun; their choice of these being regulated by personal qualities, not by the adventitious circumstances of wealth or high birth – a regard to which certainly tends to deteriorate the species, and is one of the causes which renders the noblesse of Europe comparatively inferior to the Asiatic, or rather the Christian noblesse to the Mahometan.

It has been remarked that our finest, most acute population, exist in the neutral ground, where the Caucasian and Keltic have mixed, but this may arise from other causes than admixture. Our healthiest and poorest country borders the Highlands, and the population enjoy more of the open air. Our eastern population, north of the natural division of Flamboroughead, are also harder and sharper featured, and keener witted, than those southward, who may be styled our fen-bred. There is no doubt more of Keltic blood mingled with the north division but the sea-born breeds have also been different, those more northerly being Scandinavian, and the more southerly consisting of the native of Lower Germany and the heavy Fleming. The placid-looking Englishman, more under the control of animal enjoyment, though perhaps not so readily acute, excels in the no less valuable qualities of constancy and bodily powers of exertion; and when properly taught under high division of labour, becomes a better operative in his particular employment, and even will sometimes extend scientific discovery further, than his more mercurial northern neighbour, who, from his quick wits being generally in advance of his manual practice, seldom attains to the dexterity which results from the combination of bodily action and restricted mental application. There exists continued very considerable intellectual capacity in this English breed, but however, animal part, it too frequently is crushed under the preponderance of the affording that purest specimen of vulgarity the English clown. But, independently of climate a great part of the low Englander's obtuseness is referable to his being entailed lord of the soil, under poor-rate law, contravening a natural law (see Note B), so that, when unsuccessful or out of employment, he, without effort to obtain some new means of independent subsistence, sinks into the parish or work-house labourer. On the contrary, the Scotsman, with no resource but in himself, with famine always in the vista, as much in his view as a principle of action in material affairs as his strong perception of the right in moral, and also under the stimulus of a high pride, leaves no means untried at home; and, when fairly starved out of his native country, among various resources, often invades the territory of his more easy-minded southern neighbour, where his acuteness seldom fails to find out a convenient occupation, in which manual dexterity is second to economy and forethought – his success exciting the wonder and envy of the dull-witted native.

It would appear, that the finest portion, at least apparently so, of the north temperate zone, between the parallels of 30° and 48° latitude, when nearly of the level of the ocean, is not so favourable for human existence as the more northern part between 50° and 60°, or even the torrid zone. The native of the north of Europe has a superior development of person, and a much longer reproductory life than the native of the south, which more than counterbalances the earlier maturity of the latter in power of increase. Independent of the great current of population setting south in the northern part of the temperate zone, there seems even to be some tendency to a flux northward, from the confines of the torrid; but this arises rather from the unsteadiness of the seasons, and consequent deficit of food, at particular times, than from a steady increase of population.

Note D

Our milder moods, benevolence, gentleness, contemplation – our refinement in sentiment – our 'lovely dreams of peace and joy', have negative weight in the balance of national strength. The rougher excitement of hatred, ambition, pride, patriotism, and the more selfish passions, is necessary to the full and strong development of our active powers. That Britain is leaving the impress of her energy and morality on a considerable portion of the world, is owing to her having first borne fire and sword over these countries: the husbandman tears up the glebe, with all its covering of weeds and flowers, before he commits his good seed to the earth. Life and death – good and evil – pleasure and pain, are the principles of impulse to the scheme or machine of nature, as heat and cold are to the steam-engine, thus moving in necessary alternate dependence, our moral sense, our perception and love of good, could not exist without the knowledge of evil; yet, we shudder at the truth of evil being part and portion of nature.

Note E
There cannot be a more striking proof of the necessity of a better representation of the marine interest, than the fact that our trading vessels are constructed of an unsuitable figure, owing to the improper manner of measuring the register tonnage. In order to save a little trouble of calculation to the surveying officer in gauging the contents of the vessel, the law directs him merely to take the length and breadth at the widest place, and from these lines, by a regular formula, to compute the tonnage; the vessel paying the charges for lights and harbours, and other dues, in proportion to this measurement. The result is, that, in order to lessen these dues individually, our vessels are constructed deep in proportion to breadth, consequently are sluggish sailors, and not nearly so safe and pleasant sea-boats as they otherwise would be – many a ship, especially with light cargo, getting on her beam-ends and foundering, or not standing up under canvas to weather a lee shore. The influence of this absurd measurement law is the more unlucky, as the ship-owner, from a deep vessel being, in proportion to the capacity of the hold, cheaper than one of shallower or longer dimensions, is already more disposed to construct his vessel deeper than is consistent with the safety of the seamen and security of the ship and cargo, the particular insurance of a deep vessel not being greater than that of one of safer proportions. The injurious effect from vessels being constructed on the principles of avoiding tolls or dues, rather than for sailing, will occur to every one. We need not say that all this flows from the ignorance or carelessness of the

constructors of our Parliamentary acts, consequent to defective representation.

Note F
In the case of the upper carse on the Tay Firth, there is evidence, both from its vestiges and from records, that it had occupied, at least, the entire firth, or sea-basin, above Broughty Ferry, and that about 50 square miles of this carse has been carried out into the German Ocean by the strong sea-tide current, a consequence of the lowering of the German Ocean, and of the deepening of the outlet of this sea-basin at Broughty Ferry, apparently by this very rapid sea-tide current. This carse appears to have been a general deposition at the bottom of a lake having only a narrow outlet communicating with the sea, and probably did not rise much higher than the height of the bottom of the outlet at that time.

An increase of deposition of alluvium, or prevention of decrease, may, in many cases, be accomplished by artificial means. The diminution of the carse of Tay was in rapid progress about sixty years ago, the sea-bank was being undermined by the waves of the basin, the clay tumbling down, diffused in the water and being carried out to sea, by every ebbing tide, purer water returning from the ocean the next tide flow.

This decrease was stopped by the adoption of stone embanking and dikes. A small extension of the carses of present high-water level, in the upper part of the firths of Tay and Forth, has lately been effected, by forming brushwood, stone and mud dikes, to promote the accumulation. In doing this, the whole art consists in placing obstructions to the current and waves, so that whatever deposition takes place at high-water, or at the beginning of the flood-tide, when the water is nearly still, may not again be raised and carried off.

Notwithstanding this accumulation, and also the prevention of further waste of the superior carse, the deepening of the Tay Firth, formerly carse, and of the gorge at Broughty Ferry, seems still in progress, and could not, without very considerable labour, be prevented. In the case, however, of the sea-basin of Montrose, a little labour, from the narrowness of the gorges, would put it in a condition to become gradually filled with mud. Not a great deal more expenditure than what has sufficed to erect the suspension bridge over its largest outlet, would have entirely filled up this outlet, and the smaller outlet might have been also filled to within several feet of high-water, and made of sufficient breadth only to emit the water of the river, which flows into the basin. The floated sand and mud of this river, thus prevented from being carried out to sea, would, in the course of years, completely fill up the basin.

From some vestiges of the upper carse, as well as of the lower or submarine carse, in situations where their formation cannot easily be traced to any local cause, it seems not improbable that the basin of the German Sea itself, nearly as far north as the extent of Scotland, had at one time been occupied with a carse or delta, a continuation of Holland, formed by the accumulation of the diluvium of the rivers which flow into this basin, together with the molluscous exuviae of the North Sea, and the abrasion of the Norwegian coast and Scottish islands, borne downward by the heavy North Sea swell.

In the case of the delta of Holland having extended so far northward, a subsidence of the land or rising of the sea, so as to form a passage for the waters round Britain, must have occurred. The derangement, at several places, of the fine wavy stratification of these carses, and the confusedly heaped-up beds of broken sea-shells, [show] that some great rush of water had taken place, probably when Belgium was dissevered from England. Since the opening of the bottom of the gulf, the accumulation may have been undergoing a gradual reduction, by more diffused mud being carried off from the German Sea into the Atlantic and North Sea, than what the former is receiving, the same process taking place here as has been occurring in the basin of the Tay.

The sea water from Flamboroughhead, southward to the Straits of Dover, is generally discoloured with mud; and during every breeze takes up an addition from the bottom, which is an alluvium so unstable and loose, that no sea vegetation can hold in it. From not producing herbage, the general basis of animal life, few fishes or shells can find support in it.

The large sand-banks on the Dutch and English coast – in some places, such as the Goodwin Sands, certainly the heavier, less diffusable part of the former alluvial country, and portions

51

of these alluvial districts being retained by artificial means – bear a striking resemblance to the sandbanks of the sea basin of the Tay – the less diffusable remains of the removed portion of the alluvium which had once occupied all that basin, and to the remaining portion of the alluvium also retained by artificial means.

Throughout this volume, we have felt considerable inconvenience from the adopted dogmatical classification of plants, and have all along been floundering between species and variety, which certainly under culture soften into each other. A particular conformity, each after its own kind, when in a state of nature, termed species, no doubt exists to a considerable degree. This conformity has existed during the last forty centuries. Geologists discover a like particular conformity – fossil species – through the deep deposition of each great epoch, but they also discover an almost complete difference to exist between the species or stamp of life, of one epoch from that of every other. We are therefore led to admit either of a repeated miraculous creation; or of a power of change, under a change of circumstances, to belong to living organised matter, or rather to the congeries of inferior life, which appears to form superior. The derangements and changes in organised existence, induced by a change of circumstance from the interference of man, affording us proof of the plastic quality of superior life, and the likelihood that circumstances have been very different in the different epochs, though steady in each, tend strongly to heighten the probability of the latter theory.

When we view the immense calcareous and bituminous formations, principally from the waters and atmosphere, and consider the oxidations and depositions which have taken place, either gradually, or during some of the great convulsions, it appears at least probable that the liquid elements containing life have varied considerably at different times in composition and in weight; that our atmosphere has contained a much greater proportion of carbonic acid or oxygen; and our waters, aided by excess of carbonic acid, and greater heat resulting from greater density of atmosphere, have contained a greater quantity of lime and other mineral solutions. Is the inference then unphilosophic, that living things which are proved to have a circumstance-suiting power, a very slight change of circumstance by culture inducing a corresponding change of character, may have gradually accommodated themselves to the variations of the elements containing them, and, without new creation, have presented the diverging changeable phenomena of past and present organised existence.

The destructive liquid currents, before which the hardest mountains have been swept and comminuted into gravel, sand, and mud, which intervened between and divided these epochs, probably extending over the whole surface of the globe, and destroying all living things, must have reduced existence so much, that an unoccupied field would be formed for new diverging ramifications of life, which, from the connected sexual system of vegetables, and the natural instincts of animals, to herd and combine with their own kind, would fall into specific groups, these remnants, in the course of time, moulding and accommodating their being anew to the change of circumstances, and to every possible means of subsistence, and the millions of ages of regularity which appear to have followed between the epochs, probably after this accommodation was completed, affording fossil deposit of regular specific character.

There are only two probable ways of change – the above, and the still wider deviation from present occurrence – of indestructible or molecular life (which seems to resolve itself into powers of attraction and repulsion under mathematical figure and regulation, bearing a slight systematic similitude to the great aggregations of matter), gradually uniting and developing itself into new circumstance-suited living aggregates, without the presence of any mould or germ of former aggregates, but this scarcely differs from new creation, only it forms a portion of a continued scheme or system.

In endeavouring to trace, in the former way, the principle of these changes of fashion which have taken place in the domiciles of life, the following questions occur: Do they arise from admixture of species nearly allied producing intermediate species? Are they the diverging ramifications of the living principle under modification of circumstance? Or have they resulted from the combined agency of both? Is there only one living principle? Does organised existence, and perhaps all material existence, consist of one Proteus principle of life capable of gradual circumstance-suited modifications and aggregations, without bound under the solvent or motion-giving principle, heat or light? There is more beauty and unity of design in this continual balancing of life to circumstance, and greater conformity to those dispositions of nature which are manifest to us, than in total destruction and new creation. It is improbable that much of this diversification is owing to commixture of species nearly allied, all change by this appears very limited, and confined within the bounds of what is called Species; the progeny of the same parents, under great difference of circumstance, might, in several generations, even become distinct species, incapable of co-reproduction.

The self-regulating adaptive disposition of organised life may, in part, be traced to the extreme fecundity of Nature, who, as before stated, has, in all the varieties of Her offspring, a prolific power much beyond (in many cases a thousandfold) what is necessary to fill up the vacancies caused by senile decay. As the field of existence is limited and pre-occupied, it is only the hardier, more robust, better suited to circumstance individuals, who are able to struggle forward to maturity, these inhabiting only the situations to which they have superior adaptation and greater power of occupancy than any other kind; the weaker, less circumstance-suited, being prematurely destroyed. This principle is in constant action, it regulates the colour, the figure, the capacities, and instincts; those individuals of each species, whose colour and covering are best suited to concealment or protection from enemies, or defence from vicissitude and inclemencies of climate, whose figure is best accommodated to health, strength, defence, and support; whose capacities and instincts can best regulate the physical energies to self-advantage according to circumstances – in such immense waste of primary and youthful life, those only come forward to maturity from the strict ordeal by which Nature tests their adaptation to Her standard of perfection and fitness to continue their kind by reproduction.

From the unremitting operation of this law acting in concert with the tendency which the progeny have to take the more particular qualities of the parents, together with the connected sexual system in vegetables, and instinctive limitation to its own kind in animals, a considerable uniformity of figure, colour, and character, is induced, constituting species; the breed gradually acquiring the very best possible adaptation of these to its condition which it is susceptible of, and when alteration of circumstance occurs, thus changing in character to suit these as far as its nature is susceptible of change.

This circumstance-adaptive law, operating upon the slight but natural disposition to sport in the progeny (seedling variety), does not preclude the supposed influence which volition or sensation may have over the configuration of the body. To examine into the disposition to sport in the progeny, even when there is only one parent, as in many vegetables, and to investigate how much variation is modified by the mind or nervous sensation of the parents, or of the living thing itself during its progress to maturity; how far it depends upon external circumstance, and how far on the will, irritability and muscular exertion, is open to examination and experiment. In the first place, we ought to investigate its dependency upon the preceding links of the particular chain of life, variety being often merely types or approximations of former parentage; thence the variation of the family, as well as of the individual, must be embraced by our experiments.

This continuation of family type, not broken by casual particular aberration, is mental as well as corporeal, and is exemplified in many of the dispositions or instincts of particular races of men. These innate or continuous ideas or habits, seem proportionally greater in the insect tribes, those especially of shorter revolution; and forming an abiding memory, may resolve much of the enigma of instinct, and the foreknowledge which these tribes have of what is necessary to completing their round of life, reducing this to knowledge, or impressions, and habits, acquired by a long experience. This greater continuity of existence, or rather continuity of perceptions and impressions, in insects, is highly probable; it is even difficult in some to ascertain the particular stops when each individuality commences, under the different phases of egg, larva, pupa, or if much consciousness of individuality exists. The continuation of reproduction for several generations by the females alone in some of these tribes, tends to the probability of the greater continuity of existence, and the subdivisions of life by cuttings, at any rate must stagger the advocate of individuality.

Among the millions of specific varieties of living things

which occupy the humid portion of the surface of our planet, as far back as can be traced, there does not appear, with the exception of man, to have been any particular engrossing race, but a pretty fair balance of powers of occupancy – or rather, most wonderful variation of circumstance parallel to the nature of every species, as if circumstance and species had grown up together. There are indeed several races which have threatened ascendancy in some particular regions, but it is man alone from whom any imminent danger to the existence of his brethren is to be dreaded.

As far back as history reaches, man had already had considerable influence, and had made encroachments upon his fellow denizens, probably occasioning the destruction of many species, and the production and continuation of a number of varieties or even species, which he found more suited to supply his wants, but which, from the infirmity of their condition – not having undergone selection by the law of nature, of which we have spoken, cannot maintain their ground without his culture and protection.

It is, however, only in the present age that man has begun to reap the fruits of his tedious education, and has proven how much 'knowledge is power'. He has now acquired a dominion over the material world, and a consequent power of increase, so as to render it probable that the whole surface of the earth may soon be overrun by this engrossing anomaly, to the annihilation of every wonderful and beautiful variety of animated existence, which does not administer to his wants principally as laboratories of preparation to befit cruder elemental matter for assimilation by his organs.

In taking a retrospective glance at our pages from the press, we notice some inaccuracy and roughness, which a little more timely attention to training and pruning might have obviated; the facts and induction may, however, outbalance these.

We observe that Fig. p.27, from the want of proper shading, and error in not marking the dotted lines, does not serve well to illustrate our purpose. This figure is intended to represent a tree of a short thick stem, dividing into four branches, springing out regularly in the manner of a cross, nearly at right angles with the stem. These branches cut over about three or four feet out from the division, form each one wing of a knee, and the stem, quartered longitudinally through the heart, forms the other wing. It is of great advantage to have four branches rather than two or three, as the stem, divided into four, by being twice cut down the middle, forms the wings nearly square; whereas, when divided into two, the halves are broad and flat, and a considerable loss of timber takes place, besides, the two branches afford a thicker wing than the flat half of the stem does when squared. When the tree separates into three branches, the stem does not saw out conveniently; and when divided, the cleft part is angular, and much loss of timber also takes place in the squaring. When the stem divides into four branches, each of these branches coincides in thickness with the quartered stem, and the knees are obtained equally thick throughout, without any loss of timber. The four branches, at six or eight feet above the division, may with a little attention be thrown into a rectangular bend, and thus give eight knees from each tree – knees are generally required of about eight inches in diameter, and three and a half feet in length of wing; but when they are to be had thicker and longer, a foot or more in thickness, and from four to ten feet in length of wing, they are equally in request, suiting for high rising floors or heel-knees.

The directions for forming larch roots into knees after the tree is grubbed, are also not very explicit. The stem of the tree is cut over nearly the same distance from the bulb as the length of the root spurs; this quartered through the heart (in the same manner as above), forms one wing of the knee, and the four spurs form the other wings. The same advantage results from having four regular root-spurs in larch, as in having four regular branches in oak; the two processes are quite similar, only the roots in the one case, and the branches in the other, form one wing of the knees.

We have given no directions for the bending of plank timber. In larch, the wind generally gives the slight necessary bend to a sufficient proportion; and in oak, the trees frequently grow a little bent of their own accord.

A foot-note has been omitted, stating, that the plan of bending young trees, by tying them to an adjacent tree, intended to be soon removed, belongs, as we are informed, to Mr Loudon.

We regret that our allusion to the lamented Mr Huskisson was printed off before we knew of his death.

Since this volume went to press, there [have] been some changes of scenery on the political European stage, even rivalling what has ever been accomplished of sylvan metamorphosis on the face of nature by Sir Henry Steuart. The intense interest excited by these efforts towards the regeneration of man has completely thrown into the shade our humbler subject – the regeneration of trees. We have even forgot it ourselves in the hands of the printer, while yet unborn. These sudden transformations altering the political and moral relations of man, also render a number of our observations not quite apposite, and our speculations, some of them, rather 'prophetic of the past'. They, by obliterating national distinctions, and diminishing the occasions for going to war, will, it is hoped, bring the European family closer into amity. At any rate, they have completely thrown out the calculations of our politicians regarding the balance of power and international connection as natural allies and foes, and bind the French and British together by ties on the surest principle of friendly sympathy, '*idem velle atque nolle*', which no Machiavellian policy of cabinets, nor waywardness of political head, will be able to sunder.

We had intended to bring out *Naval Timber and Arboriculture* as a portion of a work embracing Rural Economy in general, but this is not the time to think of rural affairs.

Reviews of *Naval Timber and Arboriculture*

The Appendix was reviewed in several journals the most important being a review by Julius Loudon in the *Gardeners' Magazine* of 1832 (7: 702–3). Loudon wrote:

Matthew, Patrick: *On Naval Timber and Arboriculture*; with Critical Notes on Authors who have recently treated the Subject of Planting. 8vo, 400 pages. London, 1831. 12s.

In our Number of February, 1831 (Vol. VII, p.78.), we have given the title of this work, with a promise of a farther notice. This is, however, now so retrospective a business, that we shall perform it as briefly as possible. The author introductorily maintains that the best interests of Britain consist in the extension of her dominion on the ocean; and that, as a means to this end, naval architecture is a subject of primary importance; and, by consequence, the culture and production of naval timber is also very important. He explains, by description and by figures, the forms and qualities of the planks and timbers most in request in the construction of ships; and then describes those means of cultivating trees, which he considers most effectively conducive to the production of these required planks and timbers.

'The British forest trees suited for naval purposes' enumerated by the author are oak, Spanish chestnut, beech, Scotch elm, English elm, red-wood willow (Salix frágilis), red-wood pine, and white larch. On each of these he presents a series of remarks regarding the relative merits of their timber; and even notices, under each the varieties of each, and the relative merits of these varieties. Indeed, our author insists particularly on the necessity of paying the greatest attention to the selection, both for planting and for ultimate appropriation, of particular varieties, he contending that vegetable bodies are so susceptible of the influence of circumstances, as soil, climate, treatment of the seed, culture of the seedling, &c. &c., as to be modified and modifiable into very numerous varieties, and that it is an essential object to select the variety most adapted to the circumstances of the plot of ground to be planted. This may be very true; but it is also true that extreme will be the difficulty of diffusing, among those most engaged in the operative processes of forestry, sensitive attention to these points.

'Miscellaneous matter connected with naval timber'. Under this head the author has remarks on nurseries, planting, pruning timber, and the relations of our marine.

The last chapter is a political one; and, indeed, throughout the book proofs abound that our author is not one of those who devote themselves to a subject without caring for its ultimate issues and relations; consequently his habit of mind propels him to those political considerations which the subject, 'our marine' naturally induces: benefiting man universally is the spirit of the author's political faith.

Two hundred and twenty-two pages are occupied by 'Notices of authors relative to timber', in which strictures are presented on the following works: Monteath's *Forester's Guide*; Nicol's

Planter's Calendar; Billington's *On Planting*; Forsyth's *On Fruit and Forest Trees*; Mr Withers's writings; Steuart's *Planter's Guide*; Sir Walter Scott's critique, and Cruickshank's *Practical Planter*. The author's opinions and the opinions and practices of these writers must await the patient investigator of arboriculture, and those who delight in the comparison of ... diverse opinions. This part of the book is one which has been, or will be read with considerable interest by the authors of the above works and their partisans. An Appendix of 29 pages concludes the book, and receives some parenthetical evolutions of certain extraneous points which the author struck upon in prosecuting the thesis of this book. This may be truly termed, in a double sense, an extraordinary part of the book. One of the subjects discussed in this Appendix is the puzzling one, of the origin of species and varieties; and if the author has hereon originated no original views (and of this we are far from certain), he has certainly exhibited his own in an original manner. His whole book is written in a vigorous, cheerful pleasing tone; and although his combinations of ideas are sometimes startlingly odd, and his expression of them neither simple nor lucid, for want of practice in writing, he has produced a book which we should be sorry should be absent from our library. We had thought of presenting an abstract of the author's prescriptions for pruning trees intended for the production of plank; but, on second thought, we shall omit them, and refer the reader for them to the book by the author himself.

The book was also reviewed in the *United Services Journal* 1833 (33: 457–66). This is a long review which expands beyond the actual book under consideration. The reviewer dismissed the political aspects of the Appendix:

In thus testifying our hearty approbation of the author, it is strictly in his capacity of a forest-ranger, where he is original, bold and evidently experienced in all the arcana of the parentage, birth and education of trees. But we disclaim participation in his rumination on the law of nature, or on the outrages committed upon reason and justice by our burthens of hereditary nobility, entailed property, and insane enactments.

Comments

The *Historical Sketch* 1872 is rather misleading in some ways. Was Matthew's theory 'precisely' similar to Darwin's? So far as descent from a common ancestor is concerned, the theories are similar. But Darwin goes on to say that 'The differences of Mr Matthew's view from mine are not of much importance'. But they are. Matthew accepted Cuvier's catastrophes and mass extinctions, and Darwin confirms this: 'he seems to consider that the world was nearly depopulated at successive periods, and then restocked'. Darwin never referred to Cuvier when he mentioned catastrophes, as can be seen here. Matthew envisaged, in the Appendix, the aftermath of a major catastrophe as providing 'an unoccupied field for new diverging ramifications of life'. I can find no one else having made such a revolutionary statement; not even Cuvier, who adhered to the theory of miraculous creation of species.

Lamarck, Charles Lyell and Darwin all believed the major catastrophes and mass extinctions never happened. Darwin is further misleading when he states in the 1872 *Historical Sketch*, 'Unfortunately the view was given by Mr Matthew very briefly in scattered passages in an Appendix to a work on a different subject, so that it remained unnoticed until Mr Matthew himself drew attention to it.' One has only to read Loudon's review to see that he considered the two parts were linked. The book was noticed and reviewed by Loudon the leading arboriculturalist at that time; the book was also banned in the Perth library and probably elsewhere. The Appendix was, in part, about Catastrophism but not in terms of Cuvier's miraculous creations of species.

Darwin continued, '…and he gives as an alternative, that new forms may be generated without the presence of any mould or germ of former aggregates … but this scarcely differs from new creation, only it forms a portion of a continued scheme or system'. Matthew had rejected new creations and made it clear his evolution was a *discontinuous* evolution, as Cuvier implied.

Darwin again: 'I am not sure that I understand some passages; but it seems that he attributes much influence to the direct action of the conditions of life'. This is Lamarckism. Darwin usually translated Lamarck's 'circumstances' as 'the conditions of life'. Matthew used Lamarck's term: 'circumstance-suited'. So, Darwin clearly understood that Matthew's Appendix was based on the works of Cuvier and Lamarck, with their errors corrected.

Darwin ends with: 'He clearly saw, however, the full force of the principle of natural selection.' In June 1860, Darwin wrote to de Quatrefage: '...an obscure writer on forest trees clearly anticipated my views...' Not one neo-Darwinist has ever mentioned Darwin's *Historical Sketch* of 1872, or ever written a similar assessment of Patrick Matthew. But Darwin did not understand the Appendix when he stated that the theory was 'in scattered passages'. He did not realise that the Appendix was a political-biological statement. As far as Matthew was concerned, natural selection was a universal law of nature. Matthew was a political animal and joined the Chartists. He opposed the Corn Laws because they interfered with the law of nature which involved competition. When the Corn Laws were repealed, the home market soon improved because new inventions, like clay pipes for land drainage, and various hybridising techniques, improved the quality of wheat. Wheat production improved rapidly not despite competition but because of it, and both Darwin and Matthew argued in favour of such a competitive approach.

Although Darwin tried to give a fair account of Matthew in the *Historical Sketch*, he did him no good for several reasons. At that time, natural selection was not taken seriously; in fact, it was not taken seriously for another 100 years. There was a bias against Catastrophism until the 1970s, but Matthew had stressed the importance of the major catastrophes and as a result his ideas were rejected. Darwin's 'very briefly in scattered passages' would not entice the casual reader to investigate further. The result was that Matthew disappeared from the literature until Loren Eiseley mentioned him in *Darwin's Century* (1961), but Calman's statement of 1912 went unnoticed by Eiseley. For the British Association meeting at Dundee in 1912, Calman, Deputy Director of the Natural History Museum, was given the duty of presenting some facts about Patrick Matthew who was closely associated with Dundee. Calman translated a German article about Matthew and, although no admirer of him, let slip the remark: 'it is perhaps not always recognised how complete the anticipation really was'. Although Matthew's Appendix is much shorter than the *Origin of Species*, it did contain all the relevant facts. Darwin's main comments were about varieties, geology and instinct. In 1868, Darwin expanded Chapter 1 of the *Origin of Species* and the book *Variation in Animals and Plants under Domestication* now contains all the references which should have been included in the original edition.

Matthew's natural process of selection was a universal law of nature, including political and social life. He insisted on common descent, which he probably derived from Lamarck. In Darwin's *Historical Sketch* there is this statement concerning Lamarck: 'In these works he upholds the doctrine that all species, including man, are descended from other species'; and further: 'with respect to the means of modification he attributed something to the direct action of the physical conditions of life, something to the crossing of already existing forms, and much to use and disuse, that is to the effect of habit.'

So, there is descent with modification, which is exactly what fundamental Darwinists attribute to Darwin. Darwin certainly discussed very well and in great detail the concept of descent with modification in the *Origin of Species*. Even so, he felt that this and other subjects required recapitulation and so added a last chapter: 'That many and grave objections may be advanced against the theory of descent with modification through natural selection, I do not deny. I have endeavoured to give them their full force.' Darwin certainly did, as any reader will find in Chapter 10 of the first edition, but without any mention of catastrophes or mass extinction. It is understandable, on this basis, that Darwinists consider 'the one long argument' a magisterial piece of original thought. It is also probably the reason why Darwinists pay no attention to those naturalists, familiar with the works of Lamarck, who claimed that Darwin had revived Lamarckism. This was a great achievement, but Darwin was bent on telling the world that he owed nothing to his predecessors.

Ernst Mayr (1982), of course, attributes common descent to Darwin: 'The first Darwinian revolution, that is, the theory of common descent, was soon adopted by nearly all knowledgeable biologists'. Mayr was obviously unaware that naturalists knew about the common ancestor concept in the eighteenth century. The philosopher Immanuel Kant published his *Critique of Judgement* in 1790 and it included this passage: 'The analogy of forms which with all their differences seem to have been produced according to a common original type, strengthens our surmise of an actual relationship among them in their procreation from a common-parent, through the gradual approximation of one animal genus to another.' But Mayr (1982) does attribute evolutionism to Lamarck: 'Evolutionism did not perish with the death of Lamarck in 1829'. It would appear that Patrick Matthew was the first to support Lamarck's concept of evolution from a common ancestor in his Appendix of 1831. The main difference from Lamarck's evolution was the discontinuous evolution implicit in the works of Cuvier and the immutability of species. (see Note F)

What is frequently referred to as 'Darwinian evolution' is Lamarckian evolution, which rejected catastrophes and mass extinctions and advocated gradualism as the way one species became another. The fossil record always showed that species did not change with time into different species. The sudden appearance of a species fully formed in the fossil record was what Cuvier, Agassiz and Richard Owen found. The absence of intermediate forms created a problem for evolutionists but gave the creationists grounds for rejecting evolution.

Darwin did not include political life in his principle of natural selection. That is why he described Matthew's natural selection as confined to 'scattered passages' in the Appendix. Darwin was mainly interested in varieties and only after introducing two chapters on that subject did he turn to natural selection. Matthew's main interest was in the universal law of natural selection as it applied to arboriculture and social life. We can see the difference between Darwin and Matthew in the following passages.

The very first sentence of the *Origin of Species* announced what Darwin was going to write about *in extenso* in 1868: 'When we look to the individuals of the same variety or sub-variety of our older cultivated plants and animals, one of the first points which strikes us is, that they generally differ more from each other than do the individuals of any one species or variety in a state of nature.' Now Matthew's statement in *Naval Timber and Arboriculture* (which is alleged to be on a *different* subject): 'Man's interference, by preventing this natural process of selection among plants, independent of the wider range of circumstances to which he introduces them, has increased the difference in varieties particularly in the more domesticated kinds.' As far as Matthew was concerned, this was the only reasonable explanation after careful scrutiny of the forest and tree nurseries. Darwin interpreted the increase in domestic varieties as a creative force in natural selection, which is most often regarded as a *destructive* force. Matthew's statement shows how natural selection acts as a *positive* force in evolution.

On the other hand, Darwin had searched the literature and found more and more evidence for the difference between domestic and wild varieties. He then came to the same conclusion as Matthew had 30 years before.

Steve Jay Gould (2002) does not appear to have noticed Matthew's statement, and so he attributes the idea to Darwin: 'Natural selection obviously lies at the centre of Darwin's theory, but we must recognise, as Darwin's second key postulate, the claim that natural selection acts as a creative force of evolutionary change.' Even if Matthew had recognised the positive force of natural selection, Gould would consider that he did not recognise the significance of his speculation. However, it was not a speculation but a fact – the domestic varieties are more numerous than those in nature. Matthew is then dismissed: 'Matthew buried his views in the Appendix to a work entitled *Naval Timber and Arboriculture.*'

Matthew reacted to the 1859 edition of the *Origin of Species* by quoting several passages of the Appendix in a long letter to the *Gardeners' Chronicle*. Darwin replied in the same journal that he would insert a notice in the next edition of the *Origin of Species*. He never did and Gould (2002) makes no mention of this promise but states that 'Darwin offered some diplomatic palliation in the historical introduction added to later editions of the *Origin.*' Gould does not realise he has indicted Darwin's dishonesty in failing to keep a promise. Darwin certainly kept any mention of Matthew out of the *Origin of Species* but he gave the best analysis we have of Matthew's Appendix in the *Historical Sketch*. However, Gould chooses not to quote any passage from it. Personally, I have no evidence against accepting the *Historical Sketch* as a sincere but slightly flawed analysis of Matthew's Appendix.

Patrick Matthew's harshest critics, Gould and Kentwood Wells, after misinterpreting what Matthew had written, admitted, to their apparent irritation, that he had included evolution in life's history. Evolution! Who besides Lamarck had discussed evolution around that time? Kentwood Wells gave vent to his irritation: 'Given his providential outlook, his catastrophes, and his acceptance of the traditional definition of species, one wonders why Matthew was led to embrace evolution and natural selection at all?' The answer is that Matthew was not a providentialist but a confirmed and outspoken atheist.

Kentwood Wells' essay (1973) is so full of errors that I had to spend several pages of a book (Dempster 1996) correcting them.

The error in the present context was a misunderstanding of Matthew's discussion on the difference between providence or friendly societies and charity. Matthew comes out in support of provident societies: 'The rich man, however, likes to do good in a lordly manner ... Providence, the reverse of this, works by wholesome general laws ... the rich man's charity is an unnatural interposition counteracting the laws of providence'. Wells pounced on the providence and assumed Matthew was a providentialist. The tragedy is that this essay is accepted by English biologists as the definitive assessment of Matthew, even though they are quite ignorant about Matthew.

The question has to be asked: why would Ernst Mayr, a devoted Darwinist, choose the essay of Kentwood Wells for reference rather than Darwin's statement of 1872? Was Mayr unaware of Darwin's *Historical Sketch* when he came to discuss Matthew and is this why a paper by Kentwood Wells was taken as reference? Matthew is introduced as follows: 'The person who has the soundest claim for priority in establishing a theory of evolution by natural selection is Patrick Matthew.' Mayr continues:

> His views on evolution and natural selection were published in an Appendix on *Naval Timber and Arboriculture* ... These notes have virtually no relation to the subject matter of the book, and it is therefore not surprising that neither Darwin nor any other biologist had ever encountered them until Matthew brought forward his claims in 1860 in the *Gardeners' Chronicle*.

So it is that a misleading statement gets copied from author to author.

Although Darwin's comment about Matthew's view being given 'very briefly in scattered pages' was provided as the reason why nobody, according to Darwin, had read Matthew's book, it is a mystery why Darwin would make such a statement because he had just read the book himself. Anyone reading the book *Naval Timber and Arboriculture*, would find on page after page, a discussion of the selection, planting, pruning and maintenance of trees together with the various soils the trees require for maximum growth and reproduction. One long section ends with:

> The use of the infinite seedling varieties of plants, even in those in a state of nature, differing in luxuriance of growth

and local adaptation, seems to be to give one individual (the strongest best circumstance-suited) superiority over others of its kind around, that it may, by overtopping and smothering them, procure room for full extension, and thus affording, at the same time, a continual selection of the strongest, best circumstance-suited, for reproduction... Man's interference, by preventing this natural process of selection among plants, independent of the wider range of circumstances to which he introduces them, has increased the difference in varieties, particularly in the more domesticated kinds; and even in man himself, the greater uniformity and more general vigour among savage tribes, is referable to nearly similar selecting law – the weaker individual sinking under the ill treatment of the stronger, or under the common hardship.

A similar statement is in the first sentence of the *Origin of Species*:

When we look to the individuals of the same variety or sub-variety of our older cultivated plants and animals, one of the first points which strikes us is that they generally differ more from each other than do the individuals of any one species or variety in a state of nature.

The last sentence of Matthew's above statement is similar to a statement by Decandolle (quoted in Lyell's *Principles of Geology*): 'The greater choke the smaller, the longest livers replace those which last for a shorter period, and the more prolific gradually make themselves masters of the ground, which species multiply more slowly would otherwise fill'. Decandolle was a friend and collaborator of Lamarck who would have been aware of this observation. What Decandolle was writing about is probably a very old observation, but neither he nor Lamarck could put a name to it, let alone a principle. It will be shown in the following paragraph that Matthew was the first to give this old observation and adage a name *and* a principle:

The use of the infinite seedling varieties in the families of plants, even in those in a state of nature, differing in luxuriance of growth and local adaptation seems to be to give one individual (the strongest best circumstance-suited) superiority over others

67

of its kind around, that it may, by topping and smothering them, procure room for full growth and reproduction. Man's interference, by preventing this natural process of selection among plants, independent of the wider range of circumstances to which he introduces them, has increased the difference in varieties, particularly in the more domesticated kinds.

This excerpt is from *Naval Timber and Arboriculture* 1831 which Darwin claimed was on a different subject to its Appendix.

It would appear that neither Darwin nor Mayr realised that a long review of Matthew's book was published in 1832 by Loudon in a leading journal subscribed to by Darwin. Loudon was the leading arboriculturalist in England at that time and he made it clear that the Appendix emerged from ideas discussed in the book. It seems unlikely that Mayr ever read Matthew's book but Eiseley (1959) detected signs that Darwin had. In a recent article entitled 'Patrick Matthew: forest geneticist' by F.R. Barker (2001), a professor of silviculture, it is made abundantly clear that the book about arboriculture and the Appendix are related.

It is generally believed that Darwin introduced the idea of competition for natural resources – the struggle for existence – and that this was the mechanism that kept a check on populations. There were, Darwin maintained, favourable circumstances for the production of new forms of life: only those well fitted to their environment can reproduce the next generation; only small constant mutations of value to the animal or plant would be conserved. Evolution was achieved by micromutations for which there is little evidence.

Patrick Matthew had this to say in the Appendix:

As the field of existence is limited and pre-occupied, it is only the hardier, more robust, better suited to circumstance individuals ... who are able to struggle to maturity ... those only come forward to maturity from the strict ordeal by which Nature tests their adaptation to Her standard of perfection and fitness to continue their kind by reproduction.

No wonder Darwin admitted that Matthew had completely anticipated him.

Some authors (Mayr 1982; Løvetrup 1987) have referred to

Matthew's statements as 'Darwinian thinking'. This does not enhance Matthew's reputation and, indeed, only encourages the retention of 'Darwinian' – even when it is manifestly wrong – because 'Darwinian' is so deeply ingrained in the public mind or, as Gould (2002) put it, for the sake of 'conceptual continuity'.

Both Matthew and Darwin came to an ascetic view of nature. This is Matthew, from the Appendix: 'There is more beauty and unity of design in this continual balancing of life to circumstance, and greater conformity to those dispositions of nature which are manifest to us, than in total destruction and new creation.' And this is Darwin, from the *Origin of Species* (1860–1872): 'There is grandeur in this view of life, with its several powers, having been originally breathed by the Creator into few forms or into one...' The reader will notice that there is not a hint of 'the Creator' in Matthew's statement.

The appreciation of the grandeur and beauty of nature goes back to Cicero and onwards to most thinking people. But the unity of nature was the view held by Archdeacon and later Sub-dean William Paley, whose 1802 publication, *Natural Theology*, influenced Darwin. He claimed that, at one time, he could recite many passages of the book from memory. It should be remembered that Darwin followed a theological course at Cambridge, but it is unlikely that Matthew was influenced by Paley.

The first edition of the *Origin of Species* did not have a Creator in the final paragraph and so, Darwin apologists like Gould and Mayr, always quote from that edition. Darwin's tactic of introducing a Creator softened the stark message of the *Origin of Species*. Matthew made no such tactical use of a Creator with his even starker message and so was ignored – and still is.

It is interesting at this stage to remind readers that in March 1863, Charles Lyell wrote to Darwin to say that he now realised that there was no difference between Darwinism and Lamarckism (F. Darwin, 1892). That letter had a profound effect on Darwin. Lamarck's works had been banned in England since they were published because they were dubbed atheistic. On 29 March, Darwin wrote: 'I have always regretted that I truckled to public opinion, and used the Pentateuchal term of Creation, by which I really meant "appeared" by some wholly unknown process' (F. Darwin 1892). So, why did he not alter this in later editions? The fact is that the Creator was introduced six or seven times in other editions in the

69

Origin of Species. In Chapter 7 ('Difficulties of theory') we have this statement: 'Have we any right to assume that the Creator works by intellectual powers like those of man?' Further on in this chapter is this statement: '...and may we not believe that a living optical instrument might thus be formed as superior to one of glass, as the works of the Creator are to those of man?' Darwin admitted that it was Lamarck who introduced natural laws.

Does an honest scientist truckle to public opinion? The question never arises because so few people have read the *Origin of Species* and Darwin has become a much-loved scientist. His tactics paid off.

As we have seen, in the *Historical Sketch*, Darwin admitted that Matthew's theory was precisely similar to his own. That should be the other way round: Darwin's theory was precisely similar to Matthew's, which in turn was derived from Lamarck. The similar argument of Matthew and Darwin taken to its extreme was bound to end in 'social Matthewism' and 'social Darwinism'. Just consider these two chilling statements. The first comes from Matthew's second book, *Emigration Fields*, published in 1839. The second comes from Darwin's *Descent of Man*.

> Colonisation is comparatively a simple matter, when few Aborigines are in the way, or when they are to be swept down without compunction, as the encumbering trees of the forest.
>
> At some future period not very distant as measured by centuries, the civilised races of man will almost certainly exterminate and replace throughout the world the savage races. At the same time the anthropomorphous apes, as professor Shaeffhausen has remarked, will no doubt be exterminated. The break will then be rendered wider, for it will intervene between man in a more civilised state, as we may hope, than the Caucasian, and some ape as low as a baboon, instead of at present between the negro or Australian or the gorilla.

This aspect of the argument has been dealt with more fully elsewhere (see Dempster 1996).

Mayr concludes: 'Patrick Matthew undoubtedly had the right idea, just like Darwin did on September 28, 1838, but he did not devote the next twenty years to converting it into a cogent theory of evolution. As a result it had no impact whatever'. Mayr should know that Darwin did not spend 20 years on the *Origin of Species* and over the period 1859 to 1872 added several small changes to the text of most editions. In the 1872 edition, a whole new chapter was added to meet the criticisms of Mivart ('Miscellaneous objections to the theory of natural selection).

Mayr (2002) is far from generous to Matthew; in fact, Matthew, spelt wrongly, is curtly dismissed:

> The theory of natural selection proposed by Darwin and Wallace became the cornerstone of the modern interpretation of evolution. It was a truly revolutionary concept, having never before been suggested by any philosopher, and only rather casually referred to by two of Darwin's contemporaries (William Charles Wells and P. Matthews).

W.C. Wells died in 1818 and Darwin was born in 1809, so he was hardly a contemporary. Mayr appears to be contradicting his previous limited appraisal of Matthew (Mayr 1982), all in the service of supporting Darwin's reputation as a great scientist. However, Mayr's statement has been taken out of context. In the 1872 *Historical Sketch*, Darwin was engaged in an argument with Richard Owen. In the end Darwin concluded: 'As far as the mere enunciation of the principle of natural selection is considered, it is quite immaterial whether or not Professor Owen preceded me, for both of us in this historical sketch were long ago preceded by Dr Wells and Mr Matthews'. The misspelling of 'Matthew' is probably a typing error, and Mayr (2002) copied it. Mayr (1982) considered the essay of Wells to be of less value than Matthew's Appendix but now appears to have changed his mind (Mayr 2002).

Because of the nature of Darwin's first enunciation of natural selection (the first abstract read at the Linnean Society on 1 July 1858), the late Loren Eiseley (1959) produced evidence that by 1844 Darwin was aware of Matthew's 'natural process of selection' (1831). Here is Darwin's statement in the first abstract: 'besides this natural means of selection by which individuals are preserved ... there is a second agency at work in most unisexual animals, tending to produce the same effect, namely, the struggle of the males for the females'.

When an author is adversely criticised, it is customary to include his publication in the bibliography. Matthew's book is not in the bibliography of Mayr's book (2002) and so the reader is denied any access to what Matthew had written in 1831.

Why does Mayr appear to suppress Darwin's statements when they are available for anyone to read? Darwin does not require such an approach to bolster his reputation as a great scientist. He put his thoughts in his written works and it is by these works he has to be judged. The problem is that Darwinists do not appear to have read carefully much of what Darwin wrote. It does not seem to have occurred to them how prescient Darwin was in recognising and stressing important ideas of his predecessors that others had not appreciated. Without Darwin's statement about Matthew in the *Historical Sketch* there would be no confirmation of what Calman wrote in 1912.

By 1868 Darwin seems to have lost interest in natural selection and returned to his favourite subjects: 'varieties' and 'Pangenesis'.

Stephen Jay Gould (2002) criticises the fundamental Darwinists for their ignorance of real world history as we know it today, and their persistent distortions of his theory, but in his treatment of Patrick Matthew (Gould 1983) he reveals his ability to rework Matthew's theory of discontinuous evolution, which is similar to his own. On the other hand, he also makes statements such as: 'Scholars do make a tacit pledge when they enter this exacting profession ... to honour the struggles of those who have gone before and to treat arguments with respect and integrity' (Gould 1987). So far, only Darwin has made a reasonable effort to treat Matthew with respect and integrity, although disagreeing with his catastrophic views. Gould, who does agree with Matthew's catastrophic and evolutionary ideas, seems to have attempted to obliterate Matthew.

The trouble is that Gould wears two hats: one pro-Darwin and one anti-Darwin. His colleague, Niles Eldredge, is so convinced that Darwinism is dead that he wishes to reinvent Darwin (Eldredge 1995). Had Eldredge been aware of Matthew's Appendix he would have found that Matthew had already rejected Lamarckian-Darwinian gradualism, incorporated Cuvier's catastrophes and mass extinctions, and realised their aftermath would provide 'an unoccupied field for new diverging ramifications of life'.

In Colin Tudge's *In Mendel's Footnotes* there are many errors of the kind presented in the culture of neo-Darwinism. Tudge has much praise for Darwin but appears not to have read the 1872

Historical Sketch, and so is unaware that Darwin admitted that Matthew's theory was similar to his own. Matthew is introduced with this: 'In Scotland in the 1830s Patrick Matthew summarised the gist of natural selection somewhat bizarrely in [a] book on naval architecture.' But *On Naval Timber and Arboriculture* has little to do with naval architecture. Matthew was concerned with the poor state of the national forests and the effect this would have on the building of fleets in the future. The arboriculture aspect of the book dealt with the selection of trees, their environment and their culture. As previously noted, Barker (2001) has recently praised Matthew for his knowledge of trees and their culture.

What Tudge (1999) calls 'bizarre' are political and geographic comments along with what Darwin referred to as 'scattered' passages on the principle of natural selection. But Darwin introduced extensive passages on varieties, geology and instinct. Was that any less bizarre? Tudge (1999) comments: 'Matthew (and others) who did think in terms of natural selection failed to develop their ideas.' Darwin, on the other hand, claimed that Matthew 'saw clearly the full force of the principle of natural selection'. Tudge continues by saying that 'Perhaps they did not perceive, as Darwin did, that to produce a theory of evolution that could be applied universally and was robust it was necessary to look at the natural history of the whole world'. Matthew started his Appendix with 'There is a law universal in Nature'. To stress the universal nature of his theory of natural history, he wrote the Appendix as a politico-biological statement. Darwin did not understand this aspect and hence did not realise that the political passages were equally important in terms of a universal theory.

In the rest of the chapter, Tudge mentions Darwin's *The Descent of Man*. As to be expected, Tudge makes no mention of Darwin confessing in the 1874 edition that there was nothing original in the book because Lamarck had 'long ago' concluded that man had a simian origin. Tudge claims that Darwin made few mistakes. Perhaps few – but potentially major. One was to follow Lamarck in rejecting Cuvier's catastrophes and mass extinctions which rendered 'survival of the fittest' meaningless. This error led to Darwin accepting Lamarck's theory of continuous evolution. Darwin erred also in accepting Lamarck's idea of the inheritance of acquired characters. In the *Origin of Species* is this statement: 'From the facts alluded to in the first chapter, I think there can be little doubt that use in our domestic animals strengthens certain parts, and disuse diminishes them; and that such modifications are inherited'. Needless to say Tudge makes no mention of the fact that Part 2 of *The Descent of Man* is based on John Hunter's work on secondary sexual characters.

Tudge is still of the opinion that Schwann discovered the cell. However, it has been known for some time that the cell was discovered by Remak, a Polish Jew, and Purkinje, a Czech (Mayr 1982; Harris 1999). The works of both these anatomists were suppressed by German scientists and passed their apparant prejudices to English scientists.

Biologists tend to praise Darwin above all others but it should be realised that just before he set sail in the *Beagle*, Henslow told him to 'observe and collect'. That is what he did, and the collection consisted of:

- Insects identified by Waterhouse
- Birds identified by Gould
- Plants identified by Henslow and Hooker
- Fossils identified by Richard Owen

Steve Jones (2002), apparently, has not read the 1874 edition of *The Descent of Man*. So, Jones writes: 'The study of human evolution began in 1871 with Charles Darwin's *The Descent of Man*. He showed that one species – man – to give Homo sapiens a convenient label – had evolved from apes.' Apologists for Darwin rarely mention the 1874 edition. Furthermore, Darwin mentions in *Historical Sketch* that Lamarck had included man in his theory that species descended from previous species. Man is presented as a 'bimane [two-handed] with an opposable thumb and related to the chimpanzee and orang-utan'. So far as Part 2 of *The Descent of Man* is concerned, Darwin made it clear from the very first page that his book was based on John Hunter's definition of primary and secondary sexual characters. But, like a true Darwinist, Steve Jones has not noticed this.

In Gabriel Dover's recent book, *Dear Mr Darwin*, is this statement on page 9: 'calling the process "natural selection" was a stroke of genius.' So it seems that Dover has not heard of Matthew and his process of natural selection. Dover continues with this statement, on page 11: 'I think that you and Mendel would have enjoyed each other's company'. Dover seems not to have noticed Darwin's hostile reaction to Herbert Spencer, Naudin, Robert Grant and Patrick Matthew. Why do you think that Mendel's paper lay unopened in Darwin's study? Mendel's discovery made a nonsense of Darwin's last theory of Pangenesis.

Academic biologists frequently refer to Darwinian evolution, but it is not clear what they understand this evolution to be. Morris (1998) has recently published a beautiful book about the Burgess Shale and the rise of animals. In the section 'Evolution: why no consensus?' is this categoric statement: 'The fact of organic evolution in itself is not in dispute. This is because in essence the Darwinian formulation of descent through time and co-occurring modification of the organisms, usually registered in the fossil record by anatomical changes, seems to be unanswerably correct'. If Conway Morris had read the *Historical Sketch* he would have been aware that Darwin attributed to Lamarck the concept of descent by modification.

Following the publication of his book, Conway Morris delivered a very good TV programme about extinction, and praised the work of Cuvier. One cannot praise or even mention the work of Cuvier and be a supporter of Darwinian evolution. Conway Morris, it would appear, is not aware of Darwin's reaction to Cuvier's extinctions that is in every edition of the *Origin of Species*: 'The old notion of all the inhabitants of the earth having been swept away at successive periods by catastrophes, is very generally given up'. Darwin was quite right. The catastrophes had been given up and indeed never accepted by Lamarck and Charles Lyell. Lamarck's evolution is continuous and so is Darwin's, but when Cuvier's catastrophes and mass extinctions are part of the evidence, evolution is then considered discontinuous. So what Conway Morris considers to be 'unanswerably correct' is unanswerably incorrect.

Darwin in the *Origin of Species* was aware of the sudden demise of the ammonites at the end of the Cretaceous: '...with respect to the apparently sudden extermination of whole families or orders, as of the trilobites at the close of the Palaeozoic period, and of ammonites at the close of the secondary period'. But Darwin continued to support the Lamarckian view and reduced Cuvier's discoveries to 'the old notion'. Why Darwin disliked Cuvier has not been revealed, but it caused great confusion for decades. Since 1980, when the tritium layer at the K-T boundary was discovered, it has become fashionable to discuss Cuvier's discoveries. Darwinian evolution is now considered obsolete.

However, Darwin's dismissal of Cuvier's catastrophes and mass extinctions in 1859 set academic teaching along Darwinian lines for the next 100 years and more. A fair example of academic teaching in 1950 is in Wightman's *The Growth of Scientific Ideas* (1950). Discussing the contribution to geology by Sir Charles Lyell, Wightman has this to say:

> If on the one hand he cleared the air of the wilder fantasies of Lamarck on the other hand he removed the cramping influence of Cuvier's catastrophes, the latter's explanation of the complete disappearance of whole classes of living forms by the postulation of recurring disasters on a planetary scale, was in fact a refusal to admit that any problem existed. Of such catastrophes no evidence existed: their postulation was simply the shift of a mind wholly absorbed in the delineation of 'static forms' – a simple means of getting rid of an awkward question.

The author obviously never noticed Darwin's comments about the sudden demise of the ammonites.

Lamarck was opposed to Cuvier's catastrophes and mass extinctions, but there was proof, there was evidence. Cuvier published in 1808 the results of the excavations he carried out in the Paris Basin. He demonstrated that at varying levels below ground were the bones of quite different animals and so concluded that, in the past history of the earth, there had existed a succession of different species of animals and plants. Cuvier went on to conclude that in the past there had been periods of equilibrium interrupted by violent catastrophes. His conclusion in no way contradicts Uniformitarianism and, indeed, fits into Uniformitarianism because although there are no catastrophes acting today there were repeated episodes, like ice ages, in the past. The distorted Lamarckian-Darwinian view of the history of the earth continued up to 1980 when evidence of an asteroid striking the earth about 65 million years ago convinced the majority of scientists that Cuvier's concept was right.

In his 1842 and 1844 trial essays, Darwin used 'selection' in the manner any breeder would use it. The correct selection of plants and animals became central to successful breeding in the eighteenth century. In the early decades of the nineteenth century, Knight had developed a successful technique for crossing plants which Mendel used later on. In the early years of the same century selection became involved in the commercial advertising the goods on offer. Breeders would stress in their adverts that special attention had been paid to the careful selection of goods. Selection, in this sense, continues today. But in the last paragraph of the first abstract submitted to the Linnaean Society on 1 July 1858 is this statement: 'Besides this natural means of selection ... there is a second agency at work in most unisexual animals, tending to produce the same effect, namely, the struggle of the males for the females'. This seems a harmless statement now, but to a respectable middle-class Victorian audience it should have had a shocking effect – but there was none. The first day of July 1858 was a very hot day in London and so few people turned up to the meeting, but one important person who did attend was the Rev. Professor Haughton of Dublin. Darwin's abstracts were dismissed by him as no more than an application of Malthus' doctrine and 'all that was new in them was false, and what was true was old'. Would a Victorian Catholic priest sit listening to what would be considered in those days as obscene without an immediate protest? There was no protest from anyone. Why? During the time of the readings, Darwin was on holiday in the Isle of Wight and we know from his letters to Hooker that he altered the proofs of his abstracts. Could he have added the above statement at this stage? He altered the proofs of his abstracts and sent them directly to Hooker. Darwin checked the new proofs and sent them to Hooker again, and Hooker returned them to the printers. What was read out was not the same as what was finally published. When the *Origin of Species* was published, every member of the Linnaean Society demanded Darwin's resignation.

Michael Ruse (1986) came late to support the culture of neo-Darwinism with *Taking Darwin Seriously*. The whole tone of this book indicates that Ruse has made up his mind that only Darwin is to be considered as the founder of evolution. He rests his case on a very limited selection of Darwin's works: the 1859 edition of the *Origin of Species*, the 1871 edition of *The Descent of Man* and collected letters by Francis Darwin. Why were the other works of Darwin not considered? Could it be that these other works are an embarrassment to the Darwin myth? Darwin's 1868 book, *Variation of Animals and Plants under Domestication* has, in the very first paragraph, a tribute to Edward Blyth. For the first time Darwin has added a bibliography and in it are over 40 references to Blyth.

Darwin had the greatest esteem for Blyth but Darwinists have ignored this. We know from the bibliography in Barrett *et al.* (1987) that Darwin had read the seminal 1835–7 essays of Blyth in which natural selection is the main theme.

Ruse is a philosopher and a very articulate writer, skipping effortlessly through the works of Hume and Kant, searching for any signs of anticipation. Not finding any, he passes on. Unfortunately, he did not consult Kant's *Critique of Judgement* (1790) where this statement expresses the kind of anticipation he was probably looking for:

> The analogy of forms, which with all their differences seem to have been produced according to a common original type, strengthens our surmise of an actual relationship among them in their procreation from a common parent, through the gradual approximation of one animal genus to another – from that genus in which the principle of purposiveness seems best authenticated, namely man, down to the polyp, and again from this down to the worms and lichens, and finally to the lowest forms of nature observable to us, namely to raw matter.

This indicates that the concept of a common ancestor was discussed by naturalists in the second half of the eighteenth century. John Hunter had performed his dissections by the 1780s (see Chapter 1). Lamarck, coming from this background, had no difficulty in advocating a common ancestor, which was also Buffon's doctrine.

Ruse then passes on to another philosopher, William Whewell, who, Ruse tells us, introduced the term 'consilience' which brings together many areas of enquiry under one principle. This sounds very like Buffon's doctrine, Ruse assures us, but it would seem that he did not consult Whewell's *History of the Inductive Sciences* (1847) in which is this statement: 'either we must accept the doctrine of the transmutation of species ... or else believe in many successive acts of creation and extinction'. The former was Lamarck's doctrine and the other was Cuvier's. Darwin settled for Lamarck's transmutation of species and when the *Origin of Species* was published Whewell banned it from Trinity library. The vicar-naturalist Whewell had settled for Cuvier's doctrine because all his acts of creation were 'miraculous'.

Ruse claims that 'Darwin's theory is solid'. As solid as a colander:

78

Lamarckian transmutationist, continuous evolutionist, acceptance of the inheritance of acquired characters and rejection of catastrophes and mass extinctions.

Perhaps the greatest error Ruse makes is: 'Darwin never actually used the word "evolution" in the *Origin*'. In the sixth edition of the *Origin* there are three sentences about evolution. By 1872, 'evolution' had become drawing-room conversation among the middle classes.

Ruse mentions Lamarckism with reference to Herbert Spencer who 'relied much more heavily on so-called Lamarckism, the old notion that features can be acquired through environmental stress by adults'. It seems that Ruse has not realised how Lamarckian-orientated Darwin was. In later editions of the *Origin*, Darwin, under pressure from Wallace, changed the title of the fourth chapter: 'Natural selection' became 'Natural selection or the survival of the fittest'. And it was Herbert Spencer, a Lamarckian, who introduced the survival of the fittest.

Although the English translation of Lamarck is in Ruse's bibliography there seems to be nothing but indifference to him. It is odd that the philosopher, Ruse, does not appear to have read the original French edition. Had he done so, he would have found that Lamarck presents a plausible explanation of how an ape developed into the bipedal Homo sapiens with an opposable thumb.

Lamarck's survey and classification of animal life ends with man classified as a bimane. A bimane is an ape with opposable thumbs only on the hands. A quadrumane ape has thumbs on hands *and* feet. The problem for Lamarck was: how did a quadrumane ape become a bimane ape – man?

Lamarck's evolution involved change – change in the environment, change in needs and change in habit. His speculation involved transmutation and this we now know is wrong. Today, we know no more than Lamarck how a quadrumane ape lost the power of its feet to act as hands, forcing the creature to stand upright on its feet. I have included a paragraph from Lamarck to illustrate the flavour of his thinking:

Effectivement, si une race quelconque de quadrumanes, surtout la plus perfectioné d'entre elles, perdait, par la nécessité des circonstances, ou par quelque autre cause, l'habitude de grimper sur les arbres, et d'en empoigner les branches avec les pieds, comme avec les mains, pour s'y accrocher; et si les individus de cette race, pendant une suite de génèrations, étaient forcés de ne servir de leurs pieds que pour marcher, et cessaient d'employer leurs mains comme des pieds; il n'est pas douteux, d'après les observations exposées dans le chapitre précèdent, que ces quadrumanes ne fussent à la fin transformés en bimanes, et que les pouces de leurs pieds ne cesssaient d'être écartés des doigts, ces pieds ne leur servant plus qu'à marcher.

['If some breed of four-handed animals, especially the most perfected amongst them, lost, for some reason or other, the habit of climbing trees using the feet, as well as the hands, to grasp the branches of the trees; and, if the individuals of this breed were, during several generations, forced to use their feet only to walk and stopped using their hands as feet, no doubt the four-handed animals will eventually be transformed into two-handed animals and the big toes of their feet will cease to be separated and the feet now only used for walking.']

Note that Lamarck has written about a 'race of quadrumanes' – the whole population. Over a 150 years later, Mayr (1964) wrote: 'it is now being realised that species originate in general through the evolution of entire populations'.

Conclusion

So, what kind of a man was Patrick Matthew? In many ways, he and Darwin were remarkably similar. They both attended Edinburgh University as medical students. Matthew's father died when Patrick had only done two years of the course. He had to abandon his studies because he was needed to look after the family estates. Darwin also gave up after two years because he was disgusted with the course. They both inherited wealth early in life, both married a cousin, and both were intensely interested in natural history. Mayr (1982) even notes how similar Darwin's prose was to Matthew's.

Both men had large families and lived in large houses on large estates. However, while Darwin was a smoker, Matthew was an active anti-smoker.

Matthew came out with statements like this: 'Colonisation is comparatively a simple matter, when few aborigines are in the way, or when they are to be swept down without compunction, as the incrumbling trees of the forest'. This is no way to behave. Like Darwin, Matthew had a dark side which was an inevitable consequence of natural selection taken to its extreme. Natural selection may be a principle of nature but, in human society, it has to be curbed by sympathy that somehow has crept into human consciousness.

3

The Culture of Neo-Darwinism

During the 1930s several distinguished biologists came to the definite conclusion that the principle of natural selection was the motor of evolution. A hundred years had passed since Patrick Matthew had first published the principle in 1831. The geneticists and naturalists came to agree after 'a meeting of the minds quite suddenly and completely in a period of about a dozen years' (Huxley, 1942). Historians of biology stress the fact that Matthew's statement made no impact, which is true, but these historians tend to ignore the fact that Darwin's statement on natural selection made no impact either. What had made an impact after the publication of the *Origin of Species* in 1859 was the concept of evolution, which had emerged at the beginning of the nineteenth century with the publications of Lamarck and Cuvier. Darwinists do not appear to realise how discerning Darwin was in reviving and developing Lamarckism. Unfortunately, Darwin carried on Lamarck's major mistakes. However, these mistakes should not blind us to the immense range of Lamarck's work, which led to the establishment of biology as a science of life.

The reviewers of the first edition of the *Origin* were in no doubt that Darwin had revived Lamarckism (Hull 1973). But from 1844, evolution was promoted by Robert Chambers in *The Vestiges of the Natural History of Creation* and by Herbert Spencer (1855). Evolution caught the public imagination and had been well discussed prior to Darwin's publication. Although the last word of the *Origin* is 'evolved', Darwin avoided involving evolution in his argument until the sixth edition. On three occasions, on two pages, Darwin's statements about evolution are orthodox Lamarckism – evolution by slow, gradual steps with no leaps, no catastrophes or mass extinctions.

The view of earth history which Lamarck expressed was not original. He had been appointed to the Jardin de Roi in 1778 by Buffon, who dominated biological thought in the eighteenth century. Buffon was in a difficult position because he was under the constant scrutiny of the clerics of the Sorbonne. The Church teaching was opposed to catastrophes, and Buffon, whether he agreed or not, would not dispute this. But there was another aspect to Buffon. As a young man he had visited Cambridge in 1833, to study Newton's scientific ideas, and would have become aware of Newton's fierce opposition to catastrophe theory.

The Reverend William Whiston, a biblical cosmologist, published in 1696 *A New Theory of the Earth, from its Origin to the Consummation of all Things*, and of course attempted to square his interpretation with religious belief. Whiston even considered that a comet had struck the earth and caused Noah's Flood. Newton was impressed with young Whiston and appointed him as his assistant at Trinity. So, when Newton retired from the Lucasian Chair of Mathematics in 1701, Whiston was appointed, in 1703. However, Whiston was soon in trouble with the university authorities because of his 'heretical preaching'. On the one hand he was preaching Aryanism, which denied that the Son of God was of the same substance as the Father, contrary to the ruling of the Synod of Nicea in AD 323. On the other hand, Whiston was preaching, on the basis of horrendous disturbances recorded in the Old Testament, that the past history of the earth was not as calm and peaceful as suggested in Newton's sedate 'clockwork world'. Newton, of course, was furious with his protégé.

In 1710, Whiston was sacked and Newton made no effort to save his former pupil and, indeed, supported the university authorities. Secretly, however, Newton shared Whiston's heretical religious ideas. Further information about William Whiston can be found in White (1997).

So, Newton's ideas dominated the eighteenth century. The French Revolution of 1789 changed everything, with the abolition of Judaeo-Christianity. Scientists could now state what they honestly thought. The parson-naturalists of Oxbridge were now faced with either the atheistic teaching of Lamarck or the Catastrophism of Cuvier, with his miraculous creation of each new species. They chose Cuvier's

Catastrophism, but this was abandoned when Charles Lyell introduced his *Principles of Geology* (1831–3), denying that catastrophes and mass extinctions had ever happened. This was the standard teaching in the universities until the 1970s, when the evidence for past major catastrophes had become overwhelming.

Lamarck's ideas were too atheistic for the vicar-naturalists of Oxbridge but the reason they settled for Catastrophism was because relations between two English geologists – Buckland and Conybeare – and the French palaeontologists Cuvier and Pentland were friendly and close. In addition, a Professor Jamieson of Edinburgh had translated Cuvier's catastrophes as a sort of deluge that fitted the biblical story. When the true nature of the catastrophes was revealed, Charles Lyell banished them from his *Principles of Geology*.

By the 1930s, Mendelism was accepted as an essential part of the theory of evolution. Mendelism had rendered obsolete Darwin's theories of variation (see Chapter 5 of the *Origin*). But for some time previously, some Darwinists had been rather embarrassed by this chapter in any case. So, by a sort of magician's trick, Mendelism was substituted and neo-Darwinism was introduced: a synthesis of Mendelism and Darwinism. There was some objection to neo-Darwinism but it was maintained that the reborn Darwinism (i.e. the synthesis) was still Darwinism 'in the sense that it aims at giving a naturalistic interpretation of evolution' (Huxley 1942). But this is what Darwin, in his *Historical Sketch* of 1872, claimed Lamarck had already done:

> he upholds the doctrine that all species, including man, are descended from other species. He first did the eminent service of arousing attention to the probability of all changes in the organic as well as the inorganic world, being the result of law, and not of miraculous interposition.

Decades later, the same misleading assertions are still being made. A frequent and misleading assertion is the following: 'The theory of evolution ... states that the diversity of living forms arose through modification by descent, most if not all forms having originated from common ancestors. That was the theory that Darwin established' (Thoday 1981). This is quite true, but it overlooks the fact that Darwin attributed this theory to Lamarck in the *Historical Sketch*: 'in these works he upholds the doctrine that all species, including

85

man, are descended from other species ... With respect to the method of modification, he attributed something to the direct action of the physical conditions of life'.

Julian Huxley's *Evolution: The Modern Synthesis* became the most influential book on neo-Darwinism. Needless to say, not even Lamarck's name appears in this book, and Cuvier is dismissed in a sentence. Thus the founders of invertebrate and vertebrate palaeontology are dismissed from the argument and from now on Darwin and only Darwin was considered as the founder of evolution by natural selection. Not only that, but as generations passed it was Darwin to the exclusion of everybody else. This led to misleading statements about Lamarck, Cuvier, Patrick Matthew and Edward Blyth. In fact, all the scientists that Darwin revered were completely ignored. Few biologists today will even recognise the names of Edward Blyth and John Hunter and will have little appreciation of Lamarckism.

So the culture of neo-Darwinism was born. A culture devoted to the glorification of Darwin that even ignored what Darwin himself had written since 1868. No junior academic biologist would dare object, even if he or she was aware of all the apparent deception involved. But this has always been so.

Charles Lyell made clear the position in the early part of the nineteenth century. 'But, speaking generally, it may be said that all the most influential teachers of geology, palaeontology, zoology and botany continued until the middle of this century either to assume the independent creation and immutability of species, or carefully to avoid expressing any opinion on this important subject. In England the calm was broken by the appearance in 1844 of a work entitled *The Vestiges of the Natural History of Creation.*' Junior academic biologists continue to carefully avoid expressing any opinion. Notice that in England there has been a chilly silence about the concept of punctuated equilibria that was published in the 1970s.

Mayr (1982), in a magisterial account of *The Growth of Biological Thought*, detailed the scientists who were mainly involved in the development of evolutionary synthesis. If one reads the works of these brilliant scientists, one will find nothing about Lamarck, Cuvier, Edward Blyth or Patrick Matthew. Their pupils, in turn, were to learn nothing of the people Darwin revered and respected. Not only that, but biologists came to know less and less of what Darwin wrote. When Mayr came to deal with Patrick Matthew he did not read Matthew's Appendix or Darwin's statement in his *Historical Sketch*, but referenced instead an article by Wells (1973). The tragedy is that English biologists now regard that essay as the definitive work on Patrick Matthew.

Following the discovery of Mendel's paper in 1900 there was a period of 30 years during which fierce debates occurred between the various biological disciplines. By the end of the 1930s a few influential biologists brought about and justified a modified Darwinism as Julian Huxley explains in his *Synthesis*: 'It is still Darwinism in the sense that it aims at giving a naturalistic interpretation of evolution.' It was the synthetic theory that was to control biological thought until the discovery of a layer of iridium at the K-T boundary in 1980 (Alvarez *et al.* 1980) which indicated that a meteorite had struck the earth millions of years ago. Although Huxley's *Synthesis* had banished Lamarck, his concept of evolution was retained. No one seemed to be aware of this. As a result of the discovery of the layers of iridium, Gould and Eldredge introduced the concept of punctuated equilibria that rendered Darwinian evolution obsolete. Darwin had taken over Lamarck's continuous evolution but it was now obvious that evolution was discontinuous. Hogben (1940) was one of the biologists who disagreed with synthetic theory and neo-Darwinism and here is what he had to say:

> According to the Darwinian Doctrine, evolution is an essentially continuous process, and selection is essentially creative in the sense that no change would occur if selection were removed. According to the modern theory, evolution is discontinuous. The differentiation of varieties or species may suffer periods of stagnation.

Until the 1970s the academic establishment ignored Cuvier's doctrine. But Gould and Eldredge had just repeated Cuvier's discoveries of major catastrophes and mass extinctions that had been accepted before Lyell introduced his *Principles of Geology*. It is still not appreciated that Patrick Matthew had accepted Cuvier's discoveries but had rejected his miraculous creations in favour of Lamarck's single creation. Matthew's evolutionary paradigm laid great stress on Cuvier's punctuated equilibria. From this concept Matthew envisaged that following a major catastrophe and mass extinction, 'an unoccupied field would be formed for new diverging ramifications of life'. Lamarck and then Darwin believed that species mutated or transformed into different species, but Matthew rejected this.

Charles Lyell, in the revised 1875 edition of *Principles of Geology* stated clearly what was implied in Lamarckian transmutation: 'In a word, at the end of many successive generations, these individuals, which originally belonged to another species, are transformed into a new and distinct species.'

Darwin, it would seem, loathed Cuvier who, by all accounts, was not a nice man. But there have been plenty of brilliant scientists who were not nice – Newton for one. But Darwin had other reasons for deliberately ignoring Cuvier's discoveries. He wanted to be regarded as the initiator of divergence that would fit in with his deep interest in variations in the wild. Cuvier is mentioned twice in the *Origin of Species* but not in relation to catastrophes, mass extinctions or divergence. Lamarck is mentioned once, but 'the Creator', on average, six times in each edition. Darwin wrote to Charles Lyell in September 1859 to say he was still struggling with divergence. So synthetic theory ruled the roost and few dared to oppose it. One such was D.C. Darlington (1961), who pointed out that all Darwin's theories were second-hand. There was an outcry when Gould and Eldredge (1972) published their theory of punctuated equilibria and few Darwinists have been won over – probably because they would have to revise their books. The major catastrophes are now being taught in the colleges but there are some biologists who do not accept they caused mass extinctions.

From time to time some distinguished biologist would mention what are referred to as 'possible precursors' to Darwin. When the late Sir Gavin de Beer (1961) was President of the Royal Society he lectured on this subject. He claimed that Wells and Matthew had published in obscure places and 'remained completely unnoticed'; but not, as we have seen, by Darwin. Wells delivered his lecture to the Royal Society where it was published in the *Transactions* in 1818. This information is in Darwin's *Historical Sketch* of 1872. Matthew's books were published in Edinburgh by A&C Black and in London by Longman. And yet de Beer continued, 'these works show that neither Wells nor Matthew had any appreciation of the magnitude of [what] they had stumbled [upon] or any competence to work it out'. In the *Dictionary of Scientific Biography* Wells is recorded as Dr W.C. Wells MD, FRS. He was a graduate of the Edinburgh Medical School and gained the Fellowship for his work on vision. He also produced the first acceptable theory on the formation of dew. He was physician at St Thomas' Hospital and continued research in many subjects. Darwin, as we have already seen, claimed that Matthew's theory was 'precisely similar' to his own and that 'he saw, clearly, the full force of the principle of natural selection'. It seems, therefore, that de Beer did not make a great deal of effort to gain information about Wells and Matthew.

It was Darwin who was anxious to promote Wells because he could now claim that Matthew was not the first to announce natural selection. When we come to examine the essay that Wells published, we find it is concerned with the role of a black skin in the tropics. Wells discusses several roles. There is one sentence that Darwin claimed to indicate natural selection: 'by art, seems to be done with equal efficiency, though more slowly, by nature, in the formations of varieties of mankind'. If that indicates the principle of natural selection then Lamarck was aware of it as well: 'Ce que nature fait avec beaucoup de temps, nous les faisons tous les jours, en changeant nous-mêmes subitement.' ['What nature takes so long to do, we can do quickly.']

Each generation of biologists since the 1960s has continued to ignore Darwin's 1872 *Historical Sketch*. All Gould (1983) had to say about Patrick Matthew's Appendix was, 'he buried it in his forest trees and saw no forest'. A few lines further on Gould tells us that Matthew had introduced evolution. These two statements do not add up. Who else was making statements about evolution in 1831? This was not just evolution but discontinuous evolution, because Matthew involved Cuvier's catastrophes in his evolutionary paradigm. In fact, Matthew laid great stress on Cuvier's punctuated equilibrium. From this concept, as we have seen, Matthew envisaged that following a major catastrophe 'an unoccupied field would be formed for new diverging ramifications of life'. Did Gould deliberately ignore Darwin's statement about Matthew in the *Sketch* or had he never read it? Remarks made by Ernst Mayr indicate he also had not read the *Sketch*. Instead of referencing the *Sketch*, Mayr referenced an article by Kentwood Wells (1973) that is now regarded as the definitive statement on Patrick Matthew by English Darwinists.

Another mode of eulogising Darwin is the statement from an academic who appears to be speaking with authority. It runs like this: Darwin established the theory of evolution that states that living forms descended by modification from common ancestors. The theory of evolution is directed by natural selection. This ignores the fact that Darwin, in the 1872 *Sketch*, claimed that Lamarck had established descent by modification. In the sixth edition of the *Origin* there are three statements about evolution that are completely Lamarckian. Darwin held rigidly to the Lamarckian idea of slow gradual steps, but Darwinists ignore this, claiming that the rate of evolution is irrelevant.

Another way of eulogising Darwin is to start with 'under the impetus of Darwin's work ... '. There is an example in the Synthesis: 'Under the impetus of Darwin's great work, *The Descent of Man*, what may be called the orthodox Darwinian view came to be generally held – namely, that all bright colours of higher animals which are restricted to the male sex, in the absence of definite evidence to the contrary, should be interpreted as owing their origin to sexual selection.' Arthur Keith (1949) was of the opinion that '*The Descent of Man* laid the foundation of our modern knowledge of man's origin.' Yet Darwin admitted, in the 1874 edition, that there was nothing original in *The Descent of Man*: 'In conclusion, that man is the descendant of other species of ancient, lower and extinct forms is not in any degree new. Lamarck long ago came to the same conclusion which has lately been maintained by several eminent naturalists and philosophers.'

This refers to Part 1. Part 2 of *The Descent of Man* is – Sexual selection. The first three words and the first two sentences on the first page refer to John Hunter's definition of primary and secondary sexual characters. The heading of every chapter is – 'Secondary sexual characters of ... mammals, insects etc.' Biologists have not noticed what is written on the first and other pages of the book. Darwin mentions Hunter's observation of a zebra on heat, and an interested ass that was refused repeatedly. The ass was then painted to resemble the zebra and was accepted by the zebra right away. Hunter came to the conclusion that colour was important in sexual selection. Darwin pounced on this idea, reviewed the published literature and made a meal of it. Hence the statement in the Synthesis that colour in sexual selection was all Darwin's idea.

What Hunter had added in his essay was what Darwin was only too pleased to quote: '...we have instinct excited by mere colour, which had so strong an effect as to get the better of everything else. But the male did not require this, the female being an animal similar to himself, was sufficient to arouse him.' (*Observations and Essays*, 1861.)

In another page Darwin refers to 'the illustrious Hunter' who pointed out that the female had to be courted. On this Darwin built his theory of the idea of the superiority of men over women that led to feminism that has been criticised off and on ever since.

For the idea of man's superior mental power Darwin introduced the work of his cousin Galton – *Heredity Genius*. This work concluded that '...if men are capable of decided eminence over women in many subjects, the average standard of mental power in man must be above that of women'.

The ridiculous circumstances that led Darwin to his ideas about women were based on the observations of a poor but intelligent Scot – John Hunter – who left his poverty-stricken home to occupy, in time, one of the magnificent mansions in Leicester Square. John Hunter whose experience of women and sex in English high society was nil, came to court the daughter of an upper middle class army doctor. He courted the lady for seven years. Why Hunter had to wait so long we will never know but her coyness might have had something to do with it. Darwin, whose sexual experience was nil before marriage, searched the literature for further information about human sexuality. In the end he agreed with Hunter that the human female was less eager than the male at a time when the Victorian high society doctors were of the opinion that the human female was devoid of sexual feelings.

There were two editions of *The Descent of Man* (1871 and 1874). Darwin admitted the priority of Lamarck in the 1874 edition along with other admissions that are now regarded as his 'pluralistic' view of species modification. Critics of the 1871 edition had obviously got at Darwin, who was always prepared to listen to them. Darwin's so-called pluralistic view of species modification is very vague. In addition to the effect of natural selection, Darwin (1874 edition) came out with, 'I distinctly stated that great weight must be attributed to the inherited effects of use and disuse, with respect both to the mind and body. I also attributed some amount of modification to the direct and prolonged action of changed conditions of life.' Darwin just could not bring himself to admit that all this was Lamarckian speculation – a bit of this and a bit of that! To laud this as pluralistic is not a serious claim. Darwin's 'conditions of life' was his translation of Lamarck's 'circumstances'. In the sixth edition *Origin* Darwin was so content with Lamarckism that he reverted to 'circumstances'. In Chapter 4 of that edition there is a subsection entitled 'Circumstances favourable for the production of new forms of life'. To what Darwin confessed in that 1874 edition of *The Descent of Man* is an embarrassment to the Darwin myth and so it is fashionable never to mention that edition and certainly omit it from the bibliographies. An excellent example is in Dennett's *Darwin's Dangerous Idea* (1995): 'It is clear where the theory is heading, so Darwin worked hard to produce his own, carefully thought-out version before the critics and sceptics could bury the issue in misrepresentation and alarm calls: *The Descent of Man*, and *Selection in Relation to Sex* (1871).' So, not a word about the 1874 edition that was produced in response to the critics who knew their Lamarckism. And so 'the wriggler' introduced this into the 1874 edition: 'In conclusion, that man is the descendant with other species of ancient, lower and extinct forms is not in any degree new. Lamarck long ago came to the same conclusion, which has lately been maintained by several eminent naturalists and philosophers.'

In addition, Darwin made it clear that his theory included other Lamarckian concepts that have been quoted elsewhere. Dennett (1995) continues: 'I have tried in this book to present an accurate account of evolutionary thinking, deflecting the reader from common misunderstandings and defending the theory against ill-grounded objections ... I am confident I have succeeded.' All this in spite of omitting all the work of people that Darwin admired and was influenced by: Lamarck, Edward Blyth, John Hunter and Patrick Matthew. Dennett does not seem to take account of the fact that Darlington (1959) believed that all Darwin's ideas were second-hand, calling him 'the gamekeeper of natural selection and the poacher of Pangenesis'. Poor Darwin tried to tell his contemporaries where he got his ideas from but only after 1863.

As we know, in the *Historical Sketch* Darwin points out that Patrick Matthew had stressed the importance of the direct action of changed circumstances of life. Matthew had also been influenced by Lamarck as can be seen in his frequent use of 'circumstance-suited' and 'power of change' (*pouvoir de change*). Darwin had already made complaints about misrepresentation in the conclusion to the sixth edition of the *Origin* in 1872:

But, as my conclusions have lately been much misrepresented, and it has been stated that I attribute the modification of species exclusively to natural selection, I may be permitted to remark that in the first edition of this work, and subsequently, I placed in a most conspicuous position – namely, at the close of the Introduction – the following words: 'I am convinced that natural selection has been the main but not the exclusive means of modification. This has been to no avail. Great is the power of misrepresentation; but the history of science shows that fortunately this power does not long endure.

Why did Darwin not place that statement on the first page of a sixth edition where his critics could not fail to see it? Darwin's critics did not seem to realise that from the very first sentence of the *Origin of Species* Darwin was concerned with variations and their adaptability to the environment.

Princeton University published a reprint of *The Descent of Man* in 1981. It was the 1871 edition. The editors, J.J. Bonner and R.M. May explained the reason why they chose the 1871 edition rather than the 1874 edition: 'The reason is partly that Darwin had an unfortunate habit, in his revisions, of rewriting some of the freshness out of the original work.' And so, students were carefully screened from Darwin's confessions that appeared in the 1874 edition.

Daniel Dennet (1995) likens Darwinism to a 'universal acid' that penetrates everything it touches. One can say that the culture of neo-Darwinism is also a 'universal acid' that first distorts and then eliminates any alternative to, or anticipation of, Darwinist dogma.

Maynard Smith (1982) and Geoffrey Miller (1999) continued the tradition of ignoring Darwin's source in *The Descent of Man* in their excellent works on sexual selection. It really does appear that Darwinists do not read Darwin's works; otherwise how is it possible that this strange state of affairs has come about? Arthur Keith was not only a fanatical devotee of Darwin but also revered John Hunter, and yet even he could not have read the first page of *The Descent of Man*. Keith admitted that he found the *Origin of Species* boring, and so do many other people.

Hilary and Steven Rose, the editors of *Alas, Poor Darwin*, complain that 'Darwinian' and 'evolutionary' have become adjectives to attach to almost anything. But they are not criticising the use of concepts like 'Darwinian evolution' but vent their criticism on evolutionary psychology which 'claims to explain all aspects of human behaviour' – which, we are told, has not changed since the Pleistocene. The claims of evolutionary psychology, these editors and other authors maintain, are 'not merely mistaken but culturally pernicious'. These editors are Darwinists and probably support Darwinian evolution, although in many ways it is wrong and no longer supported by modern evidence. This may not be culturally pernicious but it is misleading and a prominent aspect of the culture of neo-Darwinism. 'Darwinian evolution' is frequently used when 'modern evolution' is more relevant. An example of this is in an excellent article by Lewis Wolpert. The very last sentence is: 'It is DNA's instability that makes mutations possible and so generates variation and enables Darwinian evolution to occur – we would not be here without it.'

Every day something Darwinian is mentioned and, for some time now, the effect has been like subliminal stimulus in commercial advertising. As Darwin remarked when John Murray, the publisher of the *Origin of Species*, wrote to him about the strange term 'natural selection', 'It is in all works on breeding.' And indeed, breeders from the mid-eighteenth century had come to realise that careful selection was of paramount importance in all aspects of horticultural and animal husbandry, in order to ensure that the 'goods' were of the best quality.

Darwin was very secretive about his sources, but Darwinists rarely if ever mention this. However, if they would only read the works of people that Darwin had read, they would find that he did provide *clues* to his sources. So far as the *Origin of Species* is concerned, Darwin refused to give his sources and he justified this by defining the work as an 'abstract':

This Abstract, which I now publish, must necessarily be imperfect. I cannot here give references and authorities for my statements. No one can feel more sensible than I do of the necessity of hereafter publishing in detail all the facts ... and I hope in a future work to do so.

Twelve years later, in 1872, the sixth edition was published with an identical introduction. Darwin continued, 'I much regret want of space prevents my having the satisfaction of acknowledging the generous assistance I have received from very many naturalists.'

One might at this stage ask who provided Dr Erasmus Darwin

94

with all the information in *Zoonomia*? No biography of Erasmus was published in his lifetime and the one by Hesketh Pearson, 1930, does not even mention sources. Erasmus was a very busy and efficient doctor and so could only occasionally attend meetings of the Lunar Society, and yet he found time to write extensively on biology but not on medical subjects. His intimate friends were Josiah Wedgwood, James Watt, Joseph Priestly and the engineer Boulton. Erasmus had links with John Hunter. In 1781, during a visit to London, Erasmus attended meetings at the New Slaughter's Coffee House in St Martin's Lane where there was a club presided over by Hunter. We know he had read some of the works of Buffon. In *Zoonomia* Part 1, Chapter 39, Section 4, is this statement: 'Mr Buffon mentions a breed of dogs without tails which are common at Rome and Naples, which he supposes to have been produced by a custom long established of cutting their tails close off.'

When Charles Darwin's notebooks were found, they revealed what Darwin was reading between 1837 and 1844. Barrett *et al.*'s book *Charles Darwin's Notebooks 1836–1844* (1987) contains a bibliography of what was read. In this are the 1835–7 essays on variation by Edward Blyth, the unpublished essays of John Hunter and the works of Lamarck. If one reads the works of these people one will recognise Darwin's sources. In the *Origin of Species* the very first sentence is about varieties and is straight out of Edward Blyth's essays. In the 1868 publication about variations, Darwin mentions the name of one man – Edward Blyth – and there are over 40 references to Blyth's works, but the 1835–7 essays are not referenced. On the first page of the Introduction is this: 'Mr Blyth has freely communicated to me his stores of knowledge on this [i.e. variations] and all other related subjects.'

On the first page of *The Descent of Man* Part 2 is John Hunter's definition of primary and secondary sexual characters. Hunter's breeding experiments form the basis of Darwin's book, and he gave many clues that this was so. Darwin was, however, obsessed with his own importance and was convinced that he owed nothing to his predecessors. What he said in private was not what he said in public. His angry reaction to Patrick Matthew's letter of 1860 is in sharp contrast to the dignified acceptance of Mendelism by Correns, de Vries and Tschermak. In *Alas, Poor Darwin*, Stephen Jay Gould is wearing his pro-Darwin hat and has this to say: 'He was kind to a fault ... he never uttered a harsh word ... or hardly ever.'

Darwin was too subtle to resort to harsh words. He was an expert at dumbing down, which had the effect he desired. For many years he referred to Patrick Matthew as 'an obscure writer', although in the *Historical Sketch* he dropped 'obscure' but continued dumbing down (see Chapter 2).

'He was kind to a fault' says Gould. While on the one hand it is recorded that Darwin gave a £100 to a young Edinburgh gardener who wished to emigrate to Australia because he had been sacked from the Botanical Gardens for advocating Darwinism, when Edward Blyth, the main provider of field notes, returned to England in 1862 a widower, penniless and broken in health, Darwin did not raise a finger to help. Friends of Darwin, who were his close associates in India – Sir P. Courtley and Dr Hugh Falconer – did, by persistently calling for a pension for Blyth, which was granted. In acting like this, Darwin did not betray the fact that Blyth's essays had been of paramount importance in the *Origin of Species* and that he had received over many years important field notes from Blyth. Darwin had, in the *Origin of Species*, made this extraordinary remark about Blyth: '[his] opinion ... I should value more than almost anyone, thinks that breeds of poultry have proceeded from the common wild fowl.' Except for the late Loren Eiseley, no one had noticed or commented on this.

In a letter to *Nature* in 1911 a Mr Vickers indicated that he had read Blyth's 1835–7 essays and found that they expounded the principle of natural selection. He then proceeded to ask various people, including Francis Darwin, who this Blyth was. Even Francis had no idea, which seems very odd because he must have been aware of the remarks that Darwin had made about Blyth. However, this shows how well Darwin could hide his tracks. As will be revealed later on, Alfred Wallace based his 1858 essay on Blyth's.

Blyth referred repeatedly to 'Providence': 'I think it is not too much to infer, that the changes in colour in many arctic animals were intended by Providence for the double purpose of preserving their bodily heat, and of enabling them to elude the observations of their enemies.' All Darwin had to do was substitute 'natural selection' for 'providence'. Blyth argued for the conservation of the species and J.B.S. Haldane (1959) demonstrated that the conservation is centripetal.

Loren Eiseley was convinced that Darwin must have read Blyth's essays but could never find the evidence. When Darwin's notebooks were found, Barrett and colleagues clearly infer that this was finally the evidence that Eiseley had failed to find. However, Mayr (1982) disagrees: 'The subsequent discovery of Darwin's notebooks has permitted the *refutation* of Eiseley's claims' (emphasis added). It is difficult to understand how Mayr could make such a statement. But he seems to be determined to rule out any influence that Blyth may have had on Darwin: 'Darwin quite likely had read Blyth's paper but paid no further attention to it since it was anti-evolutionary in spirit and not different from the writing of other natural theologians in its general thesis' (p.498).

Mayr does not seem to be aware that the essays introduced the first serious investigations into varieties and, indeed, their classification. And varieties were what Darwin was most interested in, as can be seen in the first sentence of the *Origin of Species*. Blyth's essays (not 'Blyth's paper') were read between 1837 and 1844 and far from not paying any more attention to them, Darwin brings Blyth into every edition of the *Origin of Species* in a way he treats no one else. The evidence is that Blyth was never out of Darwin's thoughts since before Blyth sailed to India.

There is, however, some truth in what Mayr is saying. Blyth was not, like Darwin, a transmutationist but believed, like Linnaeus, that species did not mutate. Admittedly, Blyth believed this for religious reasons. But aside from his religious beliefs, Blyth strikes a natural selection position as Mr Vickers, Mr Richie of the Scottish Museum and Loren Eiseley detected, along with Darwin and Wallace.

Darwin was not only secretive about his sources but when Hooker and Charles Lyell sent him papers that should have been of interest to him, they were always pooh-poohed – notably Naudin's essay. In other instances Darwin would give the impression that he was 'unaware' of somebody. In 1852, Lyell wrote to Darwin urging him to put Barrande on the Royal Society Foreign List. Darwin sent the message to Huxley and went to the Crystal Palace on the very day of adjudication. Barrande was not elected (he never was) but he *is* referred to in the *Origin*.

The culture of neo-Darwinism has its roots in the nineteenth century. The 'gang of four' young men – Charles Lyell, Charles Darwin, Thomas Huxley and Alfred Wallace, all criticised Lamarck. Except for Wallace they all regretted this in their old age, but the damage had been done: in 1942, Lamarck's name does not even appear in Huxley's *Evolution, The Modern Synthesis*.

What is meant by Darwinian evolution? Although Darwinists claim that Darwinian evolution means evolution by natural selection, Patrick Matthew had already established that by 1831. Furthermore, Darwin's evolution was a continuous evolution, as established by Lamarck, and is now obsolete.

Matthew's evolution is a discontinuous evolution because he accepted the catastrophes and mass extinctions established by Cuvier.

Why did Darwin avoid involving 'evolution' in his long argument? In 1844, after his long searches for information, Darwin wrote to Hooker to inform him that he was 'almost convinced ... that species were not immutable'. Darwin was now a supporter of Lamarck but at the same time told Hooker that Lamarck's work was 'veritable rubbish'.

Vickers found that a Mr J. Richie of the Royal Scottish Museum knew all about Blyth. Richie agreed that Blyth had recognised the principle of natural selection; however, he considered that Blyth had failed in the true appreciation of the principle, 'in that he regards his principle as operating for the conservation rather than the progression of the type'. Blyth certainly did not accept transmutation but argued instead for the conservation of the species. J.B.S. Haldane (1959) has demonstrated that conservation is through centripetal selection. Blyth sailed for Bengal in 1842 and for the next 20 years sent Darwin detailed fieldnotes but never again, it seems, mentioned Providence.

In the sixth edition of the *Origin of Species* Darwin introduced 'evolution' to his argument:

> That many species have evolved in an extremely gradual manner there can hardly be a doubt... Many large groups of facts are intelligible only on the principle that species have evolved by very small steps... Everyone who believes in slow and gradual evolution will come to admit that specific changes may have been abrupt and as great as any single variation.

These are all Lamarckian concepts, yet Gould (1997) states that 'nature ... works on Darwinian not Lamarckian principles ... Acquired characters are not inherited'. As we have seen, Darwin never changed his mind about the inheritance of acquired characters: 'There can be little doubt that use in our domestic animals strengthens and enlarges certain parts, and disuse diminishes them; and that such modifications are inherited.'

In all editions of the *Origin of Species* Darwin expounded his principle of divergence of character, and did so without changing one word: 'The principle, which I have designated by this term, is of high importance on my theory, and explains, as I believe, several important facts.' In the chapter on 'Geological succession', Darwin returned to divergence of character and extinction. Here he states how a variety becomes a species: 'one species giving rise to first to two or three varieties which in their turn, produce by equally slow steps other species, and so on, like the branching of a great tree.' This is Lamarckism.

Here is Lyell's interpretation of Lamarck's concept: 'In a word, at the end of many successive generations, these individuals, which originally belonged to another species, are transformed into a new and distinct species' (1875). However, in 1863, Darwin wrote this to George Bentham: 'When we descend to details, we can prove that no species has changed ... nor can we prove that the supposed changes are beneficial, which is the groundwork of the theory.' This was the teaching of Cuvier, Agassiz and Richard Owen, who based their theories on the fossil evidence. If Darwin could still write in Lamarckian terms in 1872, it would appear he had forgotten what he had written in 1863.

Here is Lamarck's view:

> dans tout c'est que la nature opère, elle ne fait rien brusquement, et que partout elle agit avec lenteur et par degrès successifs ... qu'il n'est nullement nécessaire de supposer qu'une catastrophe universelle est venue tout culbuter et détruire une grande partie des opérations mêmes de la nature.

> ['Wherever Nature works she does nothing suddenly but always slowly and by successive steps ... it is not necessary to believe that a universal catastrophe arrived, knocked down and destroyed a large part of the works of Nature.']

And here is Darwin on extinction, in the *Origin of Species*:

> The old notion of all the inhabitants of the earth having been swept away at successive periods by catastrophes, is very

generally given up ... we have every reason to believe, from the study of the tertiary formations, that species and groups of species gradually disappear, one after another, first from one spot, and then from another.

Darwin was right in saying this, but since the 1970s catastrophes, mass extinctions and 'leaps' have come to be accepted also.

It would appear that orthodox Darwinists have not come across *The Life and Letters of Charles Darwin* by Francis Darwin (1892). There are several important and revealing letters in this collection. For example, it is frequently alleged that Darwin had formulated his theory by 1838. In 1844, Darwin wrote to Hooker, 'I am now almost convinced (contrary to the opinion I started with) that species are not ... immutable. Heaven forfend me from Lamarck[ian] nonsense of a "tendency to progression" ... But the conclusions I am led to are not widely different from his...' What is clear is that Darwin is now a Lamarckian transmutationist – and he remained so for the rest of his life.

Again in 1844, Darwin replied to a letter from Hooker asking for information about books on species: 'With respect to books on the subject, I do not know of any systematical ones, except Lamarck's which is veritable rubbish.'

There are several letters concerning the 1858 arrival of Wallace's essay. Even at that date Darwin had not got his ideas together. He appealed to Charles Lyell and Joseph Hooker at Kew. On 28 June 1858 Darwin wrote to Hooker: 'I have just read your letter, and see you want the papers at once. I am quite prostrated and can do nothing, but I send Wallace, and the abstract of my letter to Asa Gray, which gives most imperfectly only the means of change, and does not touch on reasons for believing that species do change.'

In a letter to Lyell, Darwin wrote: 'There is nothing in Wallace's sketch which is not written out much fuller in my sketch, copied out in 1844, and read by Hooker some dozen years ago'. No wonder, because the source (Blyth's essays) was the same.

In a letter Wallace sent to A. Newton in 1887, he describes how he came to write the 1858 essay. Like Darwin, he says, he had read Malthus and 'was lying in my bed in the hot fit of intermittent fever, when the idea suddenly came to me, I thought it all out before the fit was over, and the moment I got up began to write it down, and I believe finished the first draft the next day'. There is a footnote inserted by Francis Darwin indicating that the fit was sometimes 'a cold fit' and sometimes 'a hot fit'. This indicates that Wallace changed his story from time to time. Francis was quite right to draw attention to the different phases of malaria Wallace claimed to be in. Mayr (1982) relates another story:

> At the time I was suffering from a rather severe attack of intermittent fever [malaria] at Ternate in the Molucas, and one day lying on my bed during the cold fit, wrapped in blankets... Something led me to think of the 'positive checks' described by Malthus in his essay on populations.

In spite of this recollection of Malthus, Wallace did not even mention his name in the 1858 essay. According to McKinney (1972) Wallace was not even in Ternate when he wrote the essay.

Ask anyone who has had malaria whether they could think intellectually during either the cold shivering fit or the exhausting fever. I had experience in the Second World War of treating airmen for malaria in the tropics. They were unable to write a letter home, far less write a well-constructed essay at the cutting edge of biology. Wallace's essay was not thrown together in a couple of days by an ill man. Wallace did not realise that he had written about natural selection until he returned to England in 1862. When he did realise, he began to talk Darwin out of natural selection in favour of the survival of the fittest. Hence Darwin's chapter title change, as alluded to earlier.

There is another story from McKinney, 1972. Between 1856 and 1857, Wallace was reading and annotating the essays of Edward Blyth, and Wallace's 1855 essay was published in the same journal as Blyth's – the *Magazine of Natural History*.

Darwin made it clear that he was influenced by Blyth, and so the source of natural selection was the same for Wallace as for Darwin. So perhaps Darwin panicked. Why was Darwin so keen to befriend Wallace, who was introduced to all the important societies and given a pension? Compare this to his treatment of Blyth; his angry reaction to Patrick Matthew; and his coolness to Herbert Spencer.

Francis Darwin gives a good account of the meeting at the Linnean Society on July 1, 1858. Hooker and Lyell misled the secretary of the Linnean Society into permitting the reading of two abstracts by Darwin and Wallace's essay. During this time Darwin was on holiday on the Isle of Wight where he received the proofs. In sending them back to Hooker he mentioned that he had changed bits of the proof, which he was quite entitled to do, but what was read out is not what was published.

Everyone agreed that there was no discussion.

July 1, 1858, was a very hot day and only a few members attended. But an important person did attend – the Reverend Professor Haughton, a Dublin geologist. He wrote a report of the meeting for the *Journal of the Geological Society of Dublin* in which Darwin's two abstracts were dismissed as 'want of novelty'. This was quite unfair because Natural Selection and Sexual Selection were introduced by Darwin. Could a staunch Catholic sit and listen to what would be regarded by a Victorian middle class audience as bearing on the obscene? So, did Darwin add Natural and Sexual Selection when he altered his proofs? Some people regard that meeting on July 1, 1858, as not one of the bright episodes of scientific history.

There is one other letter that should be considered because it caused a crisis in Darwin's life and ended his friendship with Charles Lyell. After 30 years of criticising Lamarck, Lyell came to his senses and realised how wrong he had been. He wrote to Darwin in 1863 to say that there was no difference between Darwinism and Lamarckism. Darwin was unimpressed and replied the next day:

> You refer repeatedly to my view as a modification of Lamarck's doctrine ... I can see nothing else in common between the *Origin* and Lamarck ... I believe this way of putting the case is very injurious to its acceptance, as it implies necessary progression and closely connects Wallace's and my views with what I consider, after two deliberate readings as a wretched book, and one from which (I well remember my surprise) I gained nothing.

How could Darwin say this to Lyell, who had introduced Lamarck to him with the second volume of his *Principles of Geology*?

Darwin was ill for most of 1863. For some reason he got his wife to reply to a letter he had received from Patrick Matthew the year before. She wrote the only pleasant letter that Matthew received

102

from Down House. Darwinists seldom refer to this episode because they do not seem to be aware of the effect it had on Darwin later on. From then on there was no more ridiculing of Lamarck and in the *Historical Sketch*, which appeared in slightly modified form in the remaining editions of the *Origin*. Darwin made his peace with people he had misrepresented in the past. But Edward Blyth was never mentioned in the *Historical Sketch* and Robert Grant was only briefly referred to, although he was the leader of the London Lamarckians for many years.

There are other authors on Darwinism who consciously or unconsciously followed the path set out by the culture of neo-Darwinism. Jonathan Miller and Borin Van Loon (1992) wrote *Darwin for Beginners* in a way that reveals them as quite innocently accepting every word Darwin uttered, especially in his autobiography, which many feel is not wholly reliable in its recollection of the facts.

By omitting the works of people who influenced Darwin it is quite easy to mislead a beginner, especially when introducing what appears to be an authoritative statement 'after more than one hundred and twenty years the revolution initiated by Darwin has been reinstated and irreversibly confirmed'. This is the kind of statement that flows from the *Synthesis* of 1942.

Jonathan Miller accepted the story that Robert Grant, during a walk, mentioned Lamarck. Anyone who has gone into the life of Grant will know that there would be daily lectures about Lamarck because he was the man he most revered. It was Grant who introduced Darwin to the fauna of the Firth of Forth. By the time Darwin returned to England in 1836 Robert Grant was installed (since 1828) as the first professor of zoology at University College, London – the first secular university in England. Although Darwin lived a street or two away from University College he made no effort to renew his old friendship. This would appear to indicate that Darwin *had* been influenced by Grant. Darwin was now out to tell the world that he owed nothing to his predecessors and so Grant, Blyth and Matthew were kept at a distance. It is a very curious fact that these three all died within six months of one another, and from then on Darwin's psychosomatic illness faded and he enjoyed better health than in the previous 40 years.

Jonathan Miller appears to accept Darwin's autobiography when it describes Darwin's avoidance of Sedgwick's lectures because he had been disgusted with Jamieson's lectures when he was in Edinburgh. So, how did Sedgwick get to hear about Darwin, the geology enthusiast, although he was doing a theology course? Darwin went off on a geology tour to Wales with Sedgwick and made some important observations. We see here again Darwin's tactics of apparently trying to remove any possible attributable influence on him.

Again, Jonathan Miller accepts that Darwin, as early as 1838, had formulated the essential outlines of what later became *The Origin of Species*. But Darwin wrote to Hooker in 1844: 'At last gleams of light have come, and I am almost convinced (quite contrary to the opinion I started with) that species are not (it is like confessing a murder) immutable... Heaven forefend me from Lamarck nonsense... But the conclusions I am led to are not widely different from his; though the means of change are wholly so.' Miller must have read that letter but reduced it to 'it is like confessing to a murder' – this is how apparently honest authors mislead beginners.

Darwinists are quite happy to claim that Darwin introduced evolution although he rarely used the word. In fact, Darwin introduced evolution to his argument for the first time at the end of the sixth edition of the *Origin* in 1872. Evolution had been discussed by Robert Chambers and Herbert Spencer since the 1840s. Darwin's theory of natural selection had a cool reception, and discussion centred on evolution. On two pages and on three occasions Darwin introduced evolution to his argument, but it was portrayed in Lamarckian terms.

The three statements concerned are all in Chapter 7 of the *Origin of Species*, 1872, 6th edition: first, 'Everyone who believes in slow and gradual evolution will of course admit that specific changes may have been as abrupt and as great as any single variation which we meet with under nature, or even under domestication.' Second, 'That many species have been evolved in an extremely gradual manner, there can hardly be a doubt'. And third, 'Many large groups of facts are intelligible only on the principle that species have been evolved by very small steps'. Mayr (1982) points out that 'Darwin's thesis that the gradual accumulation of very slight variations by natural selection was the mechanism of evolution was not popular among his contemporaries.' This is probably because naturalists at the time were very sceptical about Lamarckian speculative ideas. It is strange that Mayr (1982) did not realise where Darwin got his gradualism from: 'The source of Darwin's strong belief in gradualism is not entirely clear.' Elsewhere Mayr notes that 'Lamarckism, Orthogenesis, and Mutationism are also forms of non-Darwinian evolution'.

Lamarck wrote this:

Si l'on considère, d'une, part que dans tout ce que la nature opère elle ne fait rien brusquement, et que partout elle agit avec lenteur et par degrès successifs ... on reconnaitra qu'il n'est nullement necesaire de supposer qu'une catastrophe universelle est venue tout colbuter et detruire une grande partie des operations mêmes de la nature.

['Wherever Nature works she does nothing suddenly but always slowly and by successive steps ... it is not necessary to believe that a universal catastrophe arrived, knocked down and destroyed a large part of the works of Nature.']

This is what he got completely wrong but was accepted by the establishment until quite recently on the misunderstanding that it was Darwinian.

So what is evolution?

In *Evolutionary Biology* (1986), D.J. Futuyama offered this statement:

In the broadest sense, evolution is merely change, and so is all-pervasive; galaxies, languages, and political systems all evolve. Biological evolution ... is change in the properties of populations of organisms that transcend the lifetime of a single individual... The changes in populations that are considered evolutionary are those that are inheritable via the genetic material from one generation to the next...

If anyone stressed population change, it was Lamarck. That is why he introduced the word 'mutation' (from the Latin *mutare*, to change) which did not have the meaning of the modern 'mutation'. Fishes, like the flounder or turbot, were considered to have undergone 'incomplete mutation' – Lamarck's mutation meant transformism or transmutation, which has been proved wrong, but was accepted by Darwin.

Lamarck's concept of change was well expressed on p.167 in his *Philosphy of Zoology*, Chapter 7:

Mais de grands changements dans les circonstances amènent, pour les animaux, de grands changements dans leur besoins, et pareils changements dans les besoins en amènent necessairement dans les actions... Il est donc evident qu'on grand changement dans les circonstances, devenu constant pour une race d'animaux, entraine ces animaux à de nouvelles habitudes.

['But big changes in their conditions of life lead to big changes in the needs of these animals and those changes will necessarily lead to new habits. If the new habits are sustained they will be permanently established.']

It is odd that Mayr (1982) should dub Lamarckian evolution as non-Darwinian when Darwin wrote in Lamarckian terms. Mayr gives a very fair account of Lamarck's ideas but it seems that he did not realise that Lamarck, then Lyell and then Darwin got it all wrong with continuous evolution devoid of catastrophes, mass extinctions or leaps. It fell to Patrick Matthew (1831) to correct the errors of both Lamarck and Cuvier, add the natural process of selection and produce an evolutionary paradigm that fits the modern evidence.

In discussing 'The difference between Lamarck's and Darwin's theories', Mayr presents Darwin's letter to Hooker in 1844 to prove that 'Darwin himself was quite explicit in denying any benefit from Lamarck's book.' I am surprised that Mayr should fall for this. It is important to divide Darwin's writings into pre-1863 and post-1863, when Lyell's letter arrived to tell Darwin that there was no difference between Lamarckism and Darwinism. If one now reads the *Historical Sketch* of 1872 one will see that there is no more ridiculing and that Darwin attributes a great deal to Lamarck. What Darwin attributed to Lamarck the Darwinists attribute to Darwin. The main difference between Lamarck and Darwin is Darwin's insistence on natural selection. Loren Eiseley (1959) considered that he had found evidence that Darwin was aware of Patrick Matthew by 1844.

It is perhaps dangerous to extrapolate the behaviour of many mammals to the human mammal. Yet this is what Darwin had done in basing his views on those of John Hunter. Anne Fausto-Sterling, in *Alas, Poor Darwin*, has also not noticed John Hunter when she begins 'modern evolutionary psychologists follow Darwin in arguing that females are supposed to have evolved to be more sexually reserved than the males'. Hunter's observation of a painted ass resembling a zebra led him to conclude that not only colour was important in sexual selection but also that 'we have instinct excited by mere colour, which had so strong effect as to get the better of everything else. But the male did not require this, the female being an animal somewhat similar to himself, was sufficient to arouse him' (*Essays and Observations*, Owen, 1861). There are on record numerous instances where men have copulated with animals other than the human and colour was not required.

Although Darwinists have praised *The Descent of Man* many women became infuriated with Darwin's conclusions. In Chapter 19 there is a section on 'Differences in the mental powers of the two sexes' and it is in this section that Darwin comes to the conclusion that 'man has become superior to woman'. And furthermore, 'The female, on the other hand, with the rarest exception, is less eager than the male.' If you believe that you will believe anything. Does 'eager' mean 'ready at all times for sexual intercourse'? Given the right circumstances, the female is just as eager as the male and, indeed, can be even more eager than the male.

In *Alas, Poor Darwin*, several authors have argued against evolutionary psychology. On the other hand, a counter-argument has recently been published which supports evolutionary psychology: *The Mating Mind* by Geoffrey Miller (2000). It seems that he too is unaware of the work of Hunter.

In reviewing this book, Colin Tudge says that:

The Mating Mind is an exercise in evolutionary psychology, and EP should be seen as an Enlightenment pursuit with Darwinian insights, which aims to tease out the roots of human nature. Critics of EP with their tired little portmanteau of slogans, 'Just so stories' and 'biological determinism' have missed the point, and should be ashamed of themselves. Miller is the real thing, and his wonderful book should be read by everyone with a taste for serious ideas.

So let us see what Miller has to offer. A book dealing with *The Mating Mind* will obviously have to consider Darwin's sexual selection that appears in the *Descent of Man* Part 2. Miller's opening statement is: 'The years 1871 to 1930 were one long dry spell for sexual selection.' This is very true, but it indicates that Miller is not aware that sexual selection, together with John Hunter's concept of secondary sexual characters, are discussed in every edition of the *Origin of Species*. Furthermore, sexual selection is mentioned in one of Darwin's abstracts, which was read out at the Linnean Society meeting on 1 July 1858. One wonders if Miller consulted Part 2, because the first three words are 'secondary sexual characters' and the first two sentences are devoted to Hunter's definition of primary and secondary sexual characters. The heading of every chapter is 'Secondary sexual characters of ... mammals, insects' etc. Miller is not alone, because most biologists have done the same. J. Maynard-Smith's magisterial *Evolution of Sex* (1982) has a chapter on sexual selection but there is no indication that he noticed that Darwin had based his whole book on Hunter's concepts in *Essays and Observations*.

This, of course, is in the mainstream of the culture of neo-Darwinism that demands the exclusion of anyone who might have influenced Darwin. Maynard-Smith also considered that Darwin's ideas of sexual selection started in 1871.

Miller discusses the human clitoris and orgasm with a show of authority but the fact that he has not one word to say about the glands of Bartholine indicates that he has not examined the human vulva in any great detail either in textbooks or on the live female. These glands have been known since the sixteenth century but they have only been illustrated in recent editions of *Gray's Anatomy*. What are we to do with a biologist who describes the human vulva with characteristics it does not have? 'The human clitoris shows no apparent signs of having evolved directly through male mate choice. It is not especially large, brightly coloured, especially shaped, or selectively displayed during courtship' (Miller, 2000). This in no way describes some parts of the human vulva.

Whenever or wherever constant pressure is applied, nature takes precautions. Pressure applied externally on the body will result in squamous epithelial cells laid down in those areas, which can be increased in thickness, as on the heel of the foot. Joint surfaces are protected by synovial fluid that facilitates smooth movement.

The human vulva is protected from pressure by secretion from the glands of Bartholine. Under calm and hygienic conditions the vulva is kept slightly moist. In some women of a nervous disposition the glands of Bartholine fail to secrete and the vulva is dry, irritable and even painful. Such women are obviously not eager for sex. On the other hand, foreplay involving gentle stroking of the clitoris or even anticipation of sexual activity induces the glands to secrete profusely. As a result the clitoris and the rest of the vulva is ready for the pressure of the penis and sexual intercourse is rendered pleasant. Without this secretion intercourse is either very painful or impossible. So, the glands of Bartholine play their part in solving the process of pressure and as an added bonus render the act pleasurable if skilfully performed. Obviously, some people are more skilful than others and this will determine the degree to which women will eagerly respond. The tragedy is that many people pass through life without experiencing sustained pleasurable sex. It is an act that has to be learned. There are books on the subject, the most famous of which is Ovid's *Ars Amatoria*. In ancient Rome this work came to be regarded as too licentious and the Emperor Augustus had Ovid exiled to the Black Sea in AD 8.

Miller discusses the clitoris and orgasm, but does not appear to have discussed the topic with women. Masturbation can induce a clitoral orgasm but it is not as strong as the vaginal orgasm. Some women find anal intercourse a pleasure and orgasm-producing. The same muscle is involved – the levator ani – and this muscle expels faeces which would appear to be one of its functions. When mature and sex-loving women copulate, they prefer to do so above the man. The Catholic Church forbids the woman to be nearer God than the man, so this posture is ruled out for practising Catholics. The other position is on the side with penetration of the penis from behind together with clitoral stimulation.

In Patrick Matthew's Appendix is this statement: 'The derangements and changes in organised existence, induced by a change in circumstances from the interference of man, affording proof of the plastic quality of superior life, and the likelihood that circumstances have been very different in the different epochs, though steady in each, tend strongly to heighten the probability of the latter theory'; that is to say, the power of change (Lamarck's *pouvoir de change*). What is interesting here is 'the plastic quality of superior life'. In the first chapter of the *Origin of Species* Darwin marvels at the

109

enormous extent of variation and states: 'the whole organisation seems to have become plastic, and tends to depart in some small degree from that of the parental type'. According to Matthew, 'There is more beauty and unity of design in this continued balancing of life to circumstances, and greater conformity to those dispositions of nature which are manifest to us, than in total destruction and new creation'. And here is Darwin: 'There is grandeur in this view of life, with its several powers, having been originally breathed by the Creator into few forms or into one ... from so simple a beginning endless forms most beautiful and most wonderful have been, and are being, evolved.'

It was mentioned earlier that Darwin tended to place on the first page of his works that which was uppermost in his mind. The very first sentence in the *Origin of Species* is: 'When we look to the individuals of the same variety or sub-variety of our older cultivated plants and animals, one of the first points which strikes us is that they generally differ more from each other than do the individuals of any one species or variety in a state of nature.' Here is a statement by Blyth in his essays of 1835–7: 'These simple variations occur both in wild and in domesticated animals, but are much more frequent in the latter, and are commonly observed in all breeds and true varieties.' And here is Matthew in *On Naval Timber and Arboriculture* (1831): 'Man's interference, by preventing this natural process of selection among plants, independent of the wider range of circumstances to which he introduces them, has increased the difference in varieties particularly in the more domesticated kinds.' The observation on the first page of the *Origin of Species* quoted above was recognised in the eighteenth century by John Hunter.

What Patrick Matthew had in mind when he introduced 'the natural process of selection' we will never know, but it would seem to be an active process. Had his natural process of selection anything to do with the hybridist's selection? Matthew was a professional fruit grower and would have been involved in constant hybridising. Darwin was inclined to view artificial selection as a means of speeding up what nature takes so long to achieve. Recent authors also seem to regard natural selection as an active process – Dorothy Nelkin, in *Alas, Poor Darwin*, writes of 'the eternal principle of natural selection'. Bateson, also in *Alas, Poor Darwin*, writes of the 'evolutionary process of selection'. And Ted Benton in the same book refers to 'the concept of natural selection'. Have all these 'selections' the same meaning? When a species survives for millions of years and the phenotype remains the same, what has natural selection been doing during this time? What natural selection cannot do is save the species from inevitable extinction. That is the end of it. There will be no replication. In *Alas, Poor Darwin*, Gabriel Dover states that 'Natural selection is nothing more than the one-off, never-to-be repeated, passive outcome of a unique set of interactions of newly established unique phenotypes with their local environment, at each generation.' Then Dover asks, 'Is natural selection a process?' It seems that Dover had never heard of Matthew, but the way he and Darwin described natural selection reads very much like a process. However, Gabriel Dover is concerned with 'phenotypic selection and genetic sorting' and 'On this basis, natural selection is not an active process (i.e. 'some force directly selecting phenotypes') ... not a process, as such.' Dover then refers to Dawkins: 'Darwin himself advised against the potential confusion over this issue, advice ignored by generations of so-called Darwinists, culminating in Dawkins.' Dover, of course, does not quote Darwin on this point – an omission very characteristic of Darwinists. Darwin certainly gave no such advice in the first two editions of the *Origin* but there is a statement in the sixth edition that Darwinists usually avoid. Dawkins prefers not to refer to the sixth edition because it contains the concept of Pangenesis. In the chapter on natural selection Darwin complained about the concept being misrepresented: 'It has been said that I speak of natural selection as an active power or deity...'

Here is Darwin in the *Origin*:

it may metamorphically be said that natural selection is daily and hourly scrutinising, throughout the world, the slightest variation; rejecting those which are bad, preserving and adding up all that are good; silently and insensibly working whenever and wherever opportunity offers...

What is doing all this rejection and preserving? If what Darwin has written is not to be interpreted as an active process, I cannot imagine how else to interpret it. And yet Dover maintains that 'Selection is here and now, not everywhere for all time.' Darwin seems to disagree: 'But I do believe that natural selection will generally act very slowly, only at long intervals of time, and only on a few of the inhabitants of the same region'. Then Matthew comes in with:

> [natural selection] is in constant action, it regulates the colour, the figure, the capacities and instincts ... in such immense waste of primary and youthful life, those only come forward to maturity from the strict ordeal by which nature tests their adaptations to her standard of perfection and fitness to continue their kind by reproduction.

Edward Blyth stresses how the species does everything possible to defend its stability. J.B.S. Haldane (1959) makes a very good point with his idea of selection working in a centripetal manner. 'If you consider the members of a species in a distribution curve, it will be seen that those on either side of the norm tend to disappear. This is why the phenotype of an extant species resembles closely its phenotype of millions of years ago when it first appeared in the fossil record.'

In the same chapter on natural selection Darwin has a section entitled 'Circumstances favourable for the production of new forms'. This is straight out of Lamarck's work, where favourable (favorable) and opposing circumstances are well explained. Darwin makes a statement in the *Origin* very similar to that of Matthew:

> Though nature grants long periods of time for the work of natural selection, she does not grant an indefinite period; for as all organic beings are striving to seize on each place in the economy of nature, if any one species does not become modified and improved in a corresponding degree with its competitors, it will be exterminated.

In *Alas, Poor Darwin*, Gould makes natural selection into a very active process: 'Natural selection made the human brain big.' And then: 'Some features of organisms evolved by an algorithmic form of natural selection.' Gould then admits that the concepts of punctuated equilibria render Darwinian evolution obsolete.

Although Gabriel Dover has no time for Dawkins, the evolutionary psychologist, he would probably agree with this statement in the *Blind Watchmaker*: 'Nobody thought of it until Darwin and Wallace in the mid-nineteenth century ... could such a simple idea go so long undiscovered? ... Why did it have to wait for two Victorian naturalists?' As we have seen, there is much evidence to suggest that this statement is rather wide of the mark.

Dawkins is not the only academic to make this mistake. Lewontin (2000) makes this comment: 'Had Darwin not recovered from his attack of scarlet fever at the age of nine, would we be deprived of our understanding of natural selection.' It seems, once again, that Lewontin has not read Darwin's *Historical Sketch*.

And further, Wallace did not appreciate that Matthew's Appendix was a political-biological statement claiming natural selection was a fundamental law of Nature. Considering all the crazy ideas that Wallace involved himself in, one must wonder if he was aware of all the important applications.

Matthew was actively opposed to the Corn Laws that were introduced to protect the home farmer from feared foreign competition. When the Corn Laws were abolished, English wheat prodution flourished not despite competition but because of competition. The very principle Darwin argued for the organic world.

After Darwin died in 1882, Wallace took up the banner of natural selection that Darwin had lost interest in many years before when Pangenesis came to dominate his thoughts. In 1889 and again in 1901, Wallace published *Darwinism: An Exposition of the Theory of Natural Selection*. Its opening reads like this:

> Such eminent naturalists as Geoffroy Saint Hilaire, Dean Herbert, Professor Grant, von Buch and some others had expressed their belief that species arose as simple varieties, and that the species of each genus were all descended from a common ancestor, but none of them gave a clue as to the law or the method by which the change had been effected.

This, of course, is quite true, but Wallace has omitted the only man who coined the term 'natural process of selection'. For Wallace to be claimed along with Darwin as the originator of natural selection is one of the mysteries of biology. Had Darwin referenced Blyth's 1835–7 essays he could have pointed out that Wallace, like himself, had been influenced by them. Although in his 1868 book Darwin made it clear how important Blyth had been to him, Wallace never let on about the extent to which Darwin drew on Blyth's work.

This is disappointing because in other respects Wallace was a great naturalist.

Newman (1996) found no evidence to support the notion of self-organised critical behaviour but 'what we have instead, is a picture of an empirical result – the power-law distribution of extinction in the fossil record – and its explanation in terms of a theory of extinction caused by stresses on the ecosystem'. Lamarck's 'change of circumstances' appears very similar to 'stresses on the ecosystem'. If a species cannot respond to new circumstances causing stresses on the ecosystem, extinction results. Species that have survived for millions of years have obviously responded in some way to maintain their stability. Survival seems to depend to some extent on the creative response to change of habitat.

Lamarck envisaged change over '*beaucoup de temps*' which, of course, was not appreciated by Weismann cutting the tails of mice. Mutilation was not a factor so far as Lamarck was concerned. Weismann, a German naturalist, probably got the idea from Erasmus Darwin's *Zoonomia*: 'Mr Buffon mentions a breed of dogs without tails, which are common at Rome and at Naples, which he supposed to have been produced by a custom long established of cutting their tails close off.' Buffon, in turn, got the idea from Maupertuis. In his *Venus Physique* he suggested, 'If it were tried for a long time to mutilate some animals of the same breed, generation after generation, perhaps we might find that the amputated parts diminish little by little. Finally, one might see them disappear.'

Some statements made by Charles Darwin, Lamarck and Patrick Matthew have been repeated in this chapter. The object has been to present what Darwin and the others stated and not what Darwinists imagined they stated. Darwinists rarely present Darwin's actual words, and so convey confusing interpretations. Darwinian evolution and its precursor, Lamarckian evolution, are obsolete but Darwinists ignore the reason *why* they are obsolete. What Darwin did was to pick up some ideas which he considered important, then searched the literature, reviewed it and produced a book that appeared to be all his own ideas. This applies to the *Origin of Species*, which is based on the ideas of Lamarck and Edward Blyth, and *Variations in Animals and Plants* (1868), which is mainly based on the ideas of Edward Blyth. And so on, as previously explained. In fact, the *Origin of Species* had little impact because evolution had been well discussed since 1844, when *The Vestiges of the Natural History of*

114

Creation was published and continued to be published for another ten years. Herbert Spencer, a Lamarckian, was preaching evolution at that same time.

Ernst Mayr writes (1982): 'Patrick Matthew had the right idea, just like Darwin did on September 28, 1838, but he did not devote the next twenty years to convert it into a cogent theory of evolution. As a result it had no impact.' But Matthew had already spent twenty years on his Appendix that Darwin admitted was a complete anticipation of his own theory. And with that odd statement Mayr left Matthew in limbo.

What brought the *Origin of Species* to the public was a review by Thomas Huxley in *The Times* and the notorious meeting of the British Association of 1860 when the Bishop of Oxford, thinking that the *Origin* was all about man emerging from monkeys, asked Thomas that ridiculous question. Huxley should have told the Bishop that there was nothing of the kind in the *Origin* but instead made a rather foolish reply which caused uproar at the meeting. Man emerging from monkeys *had* been posited in Lamarck's work, so perhaps the Bishop had some vague memory of someone writing about man's simian origin.

In Darwin's *Historical Sketch*, prefixed in the 3rd edition of the *Origin of Species*, is this statement by Matthew:

> ...to me it did not appear a discovery. He seems to have worked it out by inductive reason, slowly and with due caution to have made his way synthetically from fact to fact onwards; while with me it was by a general glance at the scheme of Nature that I estimated this select production of species as an *a priori* recognisable fact – an axiom, requiring only to be pointed out to be admitted by unprejudiced minds of sufficient grasp.

(The full text of this letter is printed on p.116 of this volume.)

Darwin knew where this excerpt came from and dropped it from the *Historical Sketch* of 1872, incorporated with the sixth edition. Darwin probably decided not to continue to criticise Matthew for writing such things because he knew why Matthew had sent that letter to the *Gardeners' Chronicle*. Matthew had reacted to Darwin's rather peevish letter that conceded priority to Matthew. The excerpt which Darwin plucked from that letter is its tail-end and intended to make Darwin out to be a mere plodder compared with Matthew. Here is the letter Darwin wrote:

1 April 1860

Natural selection

I have been much interested by Mr Patrick Matthew's communication in the Number of your Paper, dated 7 April.* I freely acknowledge that Mr Matthew has anticipated by many years the explanation which I have offered of the origin of species, under the name of natural selection. I think that no one will feel surprised that neither I, nor apparently any other naturalist, had heard of Mr Matthew's views, considering how briefly they are given, and that they appeared in the Appendix to a work on *Naval Timber and Arboriculture*. I can do no more than offer my apologies to Mr Matthew for my entire ignorance of his publication. If another edition of my work is called for, I will insert a notice to the foregoing effect.

Here is Matthew's response:

12 May 1860

I notice in your Number of 21 April Mr Darwin's letter honourably acknowledging my prior claim relative to the origin of species. I have not the least doubt that, in publishing his late work, he believed he was the first discoverer of this Law of Nature. He is however wrong in thinking that no naturalist was aware of the previous discovery. I had occasion some 15 years ago to be conversing with a naturalist, a professor of a celebrated university, and he told me he had been reading my work, *Naval Timber*, but that he could not bring such views before his class or uphold them publicly from fear of the cutty-stool, a sort of pillory punishment, not in the market place and not devised for this offence, but generally practised a little more than a century ago. It was at least in part this spirit of resistance to scientific doctrine that caused my work to be

*Darwin made a mistake: Matthew's letter was dated 7 *March*.

116

voted unfit for the public library of that fair city itself. The age was not ripe for such ideas, nor do I believe is the present one, though Mr Darwin's formidable work is making way. As for the attempts made by many periodicals to throw doubt on Nature's Law of selection having originated species, I consider their unbelief incurable and leave them to it. Belief here requires a certain grasp of mind. No direct proof of phenomena embracing so long a period of time is within the compass of short-lived man. To attempt to satisfy a school of ultra sceptics, who have a wonderfully limited power of perception of means to ends, of connecting the phenomena of Nature, or who perhaps have not the power of comprehending the subject, would be labour in vain. Were the exact sciences brought out as new discoveries they would deny the axioms upon which the exact sciences are based.

They could not be brought to conceive the purpose of a handsaw though they saw its action, if the whole individual building it assisted to construct were not presented complete before their eyes, and even then they would deny that the senses could be trusted. Like the child looking upon the motion of a wheel in an engine they would only perceive and admire, and have their eyes dazzled and fascinated with the rapid and circular motion of the wheel, without noticing its agency in connection with the modifying power towards affecting the purposed end. Out of this class there could arise no Cuvier, able from a small fragmentary bone to determine the character and position in Nature of the extinct animal. To observers of Nature aware of the extent of the modifying power of man over organic life, and its variations in anterior time, not fettered by early prejudices, not biased by college-taught or closet-bred ideas, but with judgement free to act upon a comprehensive survey of Nature past and present, and a grasp of mind able to digest and generalise, I think that few will not see intuitively as a self-evident fact, almost without an effort of concentrated thought. Mr Darwin here seems to have more merit in the discovery than I have had – to me it did not appear a discovery. He seems to have worked it out by inductive reason, slowly and with due caution to have made his way synthetically from fact to fact onwards; while with me it was by general glance at the scheme of Nature that I estimated this select production of species as an *a priori* recognisable fact – an axiom, requiring only to be pointed out to be admitted by unprejudiced minds of sufficient grasp.

Patrick Matthew, Gourdiehill Farm, 2 May 1860

Mathew should never have written the last sentence in those terms. It was a boastful gaffe initiated by Darwin's letter. His *a priori* claim was not even true because his Appendix is based on the work of Lamarck and Cuvier.

Matthew was well-read, well-travelled, and fluent in French and German, and so must have had some knowledge of the history of *a priorism*. The question, discussed openly by Scottish and by German philosophers since the days of David Hume and Kant, was what, or how much, can we know *a priori*? And the answer is: nothing.

C. Leon Harris (1981) did not know where Darwin had found Matthew's statement, and also wondered why Matthew had not advertised his book more: 'This raises the question of why Matthew allowed his theory to remain buried for nearly three decades'. As Matthew himself noted, 'the age was not ripe for such ideas'. In addition, within the year, Lyell published Volume 2 of *Principles of Geology*, with its convincing arguments against evolution (or Lamarckism as it then became known), and it is possible that this may have discouraged Matthew from pursuing his own theory.

Unusually, it appears that *Harris* was aware of Matthew's Appendix so should have known that there was no hint of *a priorism* in it. However, he does not seem to appreciate that it is a political-biological statement. Darwin did the same when he wrote about Matthew's evolution in 'scattered passages'. Having read the Appendix, one wonders why Harris judges Matthew's inductive ability by a few sentences at the tail-end of a letter by an old and angry man? Well, that is an example of why neo-Darwinism has succeeded.

That is not the end to Matthew's *a priori* statement. Taking the statement in isolation and out of context, Ahouse (1998) quite rightly demanded from a theory more than Matthew had indicated. Ahouse, it seems, had never read Matthew's Appendix, otherwise he would have realised that Matthew's theory had more meat to it. The end result was that another scientist downgraded Patrick Matthew. Poor Darwin's *Historical Sketch* of 1872 was ignored again.

118

Ahouse (1998) introduces Matthew's *a priori* statement in an essay dealing with and criticising similar selectionist views in Dennett's (1995) *Darwin's Dangerous Idea*. Ahouse had come across the *a priori* gaffe in the *Historical Sketch* incorporated in the third edition of the *Origin of Species*, but did not realise that Darwin then omitted the gaffe in the *Historical Sketch* incorporated in the sixth edition of 1872. Because Darwin had conceded priority to Matthew, Ahouse suggests that 'Darwin's dangerous idea' should in fact be called 'Matthew's dangerous idea'. This is not as absurd as it may sound to some Darwinists. Dennett sets up natural selection as an algorithm based on Darwin having discovered 'the power of an algorithm'. Dennett defines an algorithm as 'a sort of process that can be counted on – logically – to yield a certain sort of result'. So it is a *process*. And in 1831, as you will recall, Matthew wrote of a 'natural process of selection among plants'. Darwin *never* mentioned a process; the nearest he came to one is in the first abstract read at the notorious meeting at the Linnean Society on 1 July 1858.

Dennett continues:

What Darwin discovered was not really one algorithm but, rather, a large class of related algorithms that he had no clear way to distinguish. We can now formulate his fundamental idea as follows: Life on earth has been generated over billions of years in a single branching tree – The Tree of Life – by one algorithmic process or another.

Dennett seems not to be aware of the four main branches of animal life demonstrated by Cuvier or Lamarck's evolutionary theory. These four branches removed the chain of being from biological thought. John Hunter, with his *Comparative Anatomy*, had no time for the chain of being.

Dennett might consider consulting Lamarcks *Philosophy of Zoology* to appreciate his evolutionary ideas that Darwin then quoted, virtually word for word, in the sixth edition of the *Origin of Species*.

Dennett quotes the summary of Chapter 4 of the *Origin of Species* with some parts in bold face: 'I think it would be a most extraordinary fact if no variation ever had occurred useful to each being's welfare.' This deduction Dennett claims to be 'short and sweet', but unlike

Matthew's *a priori* statement it is supported by 'one long argument', and so it seems that Dennett did not realise that Darwin had acknowledged Matthew's 'complete anticipation'.

Matthew's approach was rather different in that he regarded beneficial changes as a bonus: 'those only come forward to maturity from the strict ordeal by which Nature tests their adaptation to her standard of perfection and fitness to continue their kind by reproduction' (1831). Selection does not act by seeking out useful and beneficial changes. They only come when the life-form passes nature's tests. The difference between the number of domestic and wild varieties is a fact, so further proof is not required. What is required is the establishment of the real reason for the difference and, so far, the most plausible reason is the process of natural selection established by Patrick Matthew in 1831.

Having analysed Dennett's note on algorithms, Ahouse (1998) concludes that 'Dennett never makes it clear what we gain by his attenuated and all-embracing algorithmic conception'. Darwin's 'one long argument' involves several chapters on varieties together with something on instinct and geology derived from a review of the literature. There is also a lot of repetition. I have lost count of the number of times Darwin defines natural selection. Here is one such definition with which Matthew would probably not quite agree: 'This principle of preservation, I have called, for the sake of brevity, natural selection'.

Another author who has followed the tradition of ignoring the works of those people who influenced Darwin is Jean Gayon in his book *Darwinism's Struggle for Existence*. There really has not been much of a struggle for Darwinism since 1942. What can be said is that any opposing views have been suppressed or wrongly reviewed. Take out Darlington's *Darwin's place in History* (1961) and one can search in vain for any others until the 1970s, when Gould and Eldredge criticised the *Synthesis*.

Looking back over the last two centuries one is struck by an apparent lack of honesty among the main players. The young Darwin of 1844 was not the same Darwin of 1868. The letter from Charles Lyell in 1863 had its effect. One reads with dismay the way Robert Grant and Gideon Mantell were treated by Richard Owen and also of Cuvier's attacks on Lamarck. Owen and Cuvier were possessed of brilliant minds vitiated by a vindictiveness that knew no bounds. It has been recorded in this chapter the way three senior Harvard

120

biologists mistreated Patrick Matthew. Darwin's view of evolution is obsolete but the view Patrick Matthew presented in 1831 is now the accepted one.

There is another instance of biologists behaving badly. The biologists de Vries, Correns and Tschermak are usually credited with the discovery of Mendel's paper – *Versuche uber Pflanzen-Hybriden* (1866) – in 1900. Ernst Mayr (1982) remarked that some people, at that time, were sceptical about the veracity of their having discovered Mendel's paper after they had completed their own hybrid experiments. A Harvard biologist called Weinstein (1977) found that several biologists, named in his paper, knew all about and had discussed Mendel's paper as far back as 1872. This information came to light when Weinstein was searching the *Guide to the Literature of Botany* published in 1881 by the bibliographer D.B. Jackson.

All three biologists cited Focke's book, *Pflanzen-Michlage*, as their source for Mendel's paper. This book was published in 1881 and obviously earlier because Darwin sent his copy to G.T. Romanes in November 1880. Weinstein's investigations led him to believe that the three rediscoverers of Mendel's paper were aware of it long before 1900 because they had started their experiments about 1894. 'Why was the citation overlooked?' asked Weinstein, and concluded: 'For Mendel's paper most readers had nothing more to go on than the title as given in the *Guide*.'

It is not known when Darwin received a copy of Mendel's paper. Darwin was very interested in hybridism and, indeed, became embroiled in an argument about the veracity of the works of the great hybridiser, Gartner. Here, then, arrives a paper on a subject dear to Darwin and yet he never opened it.

Steve Jones (1999) decided to update the 1859 edition of *Origin of Species*. What is the point of updating the *Origin* when only the first edition is so treated? Darwin made small changes in each edition up to the sixth. In this last edition an extra chapter was added in order to fend off Mivart. In addition it was only in the sixth edition that Darwin involved 'evolution' in his argument. On two pages in the new chapter. 'Miscellaneous objections to the theory of natural selection', Darwin set out his view of evolution, and it is Lamarckian. However, Steve Jones (2002) does not update Darwin's attitude to extinction which, again, is Lamarckian – no catastrophes, mass extinctions or leaps. And it is in the first edition of the *Origin* that Darwin reduced Cuvier's catastrophes and mass extinctions to 'the old notion ... generally given up'. It was Charles Lyell who ignored Cuvier's discoveries and after 1831 the 'old notion' disappeared from the literature until 1980.

It so happens that another Darwinist has discussed *The Descent of Man*. Richard Dawkins (2003) included an essay on *The Descent of Man* but again there is no sign of his having accepted that Darwin based his book on John Hunter's essay on secondary sexual characters. Darwin had the highest esteem for Hunter, and the genius of Darwin was his ability to pick up an idea and consider it important when others had failed to recognise it as such.

In a very interesting book called *The Origins of Life* by John Maynard Smith and Eörs Szathmáry, we have: 'This book is an account of the evolution of complexity. Although essentially Darwinian, it would seem very strange to Darwin...'. If anyone was concerned with complexity of life it was Lamarck, who claimed in his *Philosophy of Zoology* that all living things show a tendency to complexity. Lamarck postulated that the lowest forms of life were the *infusoires*, which it was considered to have emerged spontaneously. He went on to say that complexity becomes modified by external circumstances. In the *Origin*, Darwin used these *exact* words. Lamarck considered that if there are no disturbing circumstances, then complexity is linear and regular. If there are disturbing circumstances, then change occurs. There is a whole chapter on this subject in Lamarck's book.

Although Lamarck made many mistakes which were carried on by Lyell and Darwin, it should be acknowledged that he was a great scientist. He was a world-class botanist before he was a world-class zoologist and became founder of invertebrate palaeontology. Darwin claimed that Lamarck 'first did the eminent service of arousing attention to the probability of all change in the organic, as well as in the inorganic, world, being the result of law, and not of miraculous intervention'. That was a major step in developing the theory of evolution. Lamarck was also the author of a dictionary of botany and many other botanical and meteorological works. He was one of the three great taxonomists, the other two being Linnaeus and Cuvier. Although Lamarck occupied important positions in Paris, he never had a well-paid job. In 1824 he was so short of money that he sold his herbarium, but the Museum of Paris bought it back in 1886. Lamarck (1744–1829) was buried at

Montparnasse Cemetery but the tomb disappeared in the Revolution of 1830, so it is considered that his remains went into a common grave.

4

Another Look at the Origin of Species

A citation analysis of the *Origin of Species* has in second place 'the Creator'. Decandolle is in first place.

Following the French Revolution of 1789 there was a scientific explosion in France. In the next four decades there was intense research in all the sciences as well as the beginning of Egyptology. All this hectic activity ensued without any religious intervention because the Revolution had abolished Judaeo-Christian religion. There was, however, one great disagreement between Lamarck (an atheist) and Cuvier (a religious hypocrite but a brilliant scientist). Cuvier believed in Holy Writ. In spite of this, these two scientists laid the basis of evolutionary theory. In England during this time there was a chilly silence because the Pitt government, to counter French atheism, introduced a series of Acts which ensured that Holy Writ was rigidly adhered to on pain of death or transportation for life. All scientific conclusions would be required to square with Holy Writ. Such was the position at Oxbridge universities where all the students and lecturers were communicants of the Church of England. In Scotland the situation was different because the Scottish Enlightenment proceeded *pari pasu* with the French Encyclopaedists during the years preceding the Revolution in France. So, *l'éclairecissement* was produced. In Germany the intellectuals became involved when David Hume's philosophy stimulated Kant to write *Auf Kralüng*, and the *Iluminoso* got under way in Italy, starting at Naples. So, the Enlightenment spread to every European country save Spain and Ireland.

The French intellectuals were stimulated by the *Cyclopaedia* written by the Scott, Ephraim Chambers, and translated into

125

French in 1751 and then further developed by Diderot with his *L'Encyclopaedia*.

The Scottish Enlighteners, mainly attached to Glasgow University, developed a bias against organised religion as it obtained in the Church. Adam Smith, as professor at the university, proposed the abolition of morning prayers at the university. Smith had been to Balliol College, Oxford, as a Snell Exhibitioner (1740–6). He became disgusted with the backwardness of the subjects taught compared with those at Glasgow University. It was at Balliol that he developed an anti-religious bias, which became part of his Enlightenment activity on returning to Glasgow. Religion was the enemy of the Enlightenment. It was science that Smith and the other Enlighteners looked to as the benefactor of mankind. It was this attitude to science that produced all the new advances in academic as well as industrial life. This is the reason why the Scots were the leaders of the new geology and evolutionary studies. Yet there is not a hint of this in the *Origin of Species*.

Cuvier's Catastrophism with its miraculous creation of species was accepted in England until in 1831, when Charles Lyell, an émigré Scot, introduced Uniformitarianism which dispensed with Cuvier's series of catastrophes and mass extinctions of animals and plants during the past history of the earth. Lyell was a religious man, and so in Volume 2 of his *Principles of Geology* (1832) he denounced Lamarck who considered man as just another class of mammal. So for the next thirty years until 1863, Lyell believed in the miraculous creation and fixity of species and so did everyone at Oxbridge. Only Robert Grant, as Professor of Zoology at University College London, continued to lecture on Lamarckism. When Darwin was in Edinburgh, Grant introduced him to the fauna of the Firth of Forth and Lamarckism. When he came to settle in London after the voyage on the *Beagle*, Darwin ignored Grant. For the rest of his life Darwin would make every effort to dissociate himself from anyone who could have had any influence on him. However, he could not dispense with Charles Lyell.

Lyell was instrumental in having the *Origin of Species* published in 1859 because the publisher did not like the form it was in – an Abstract with few references. Lyell's authority saw to it that this objection would be waived. Accepting Lyell's Uniformitarianism, Darwin dismissed from the *Origin of Species* any acknowledgement of catastrophes, such as the Ice Ages causing mass extinctions followed by periods of rapid speciation and then a steady state for millions of years. All six editions (1859–72) of the *Origin of Species* dispensed with Cuvier's evidence of past disasters, and in so doing gave a completely misleading account of the history of the earth. Agassiz described the Ice Ages in the 1840s but believed in the Creator, so it was inevitable that he would reject the message in the *Origin of Species*. After reading only a small part of the *Origin* he remarked: 'it is poor – very poor'. These were the identical words Darwin used in deriding Lamarck's *Philosophy of Zoology* prior to 1859. So the confusion continued throughout the nineteenth century.

In 1831, Patrick Matthew, the Scottish fruit farmer, published *Naval Timber and Arboriculture* with its Appendix outlining the very latest modern thinking about the past history of the earth. As an atheist he rejected Cuvier's miraculous birth of species. He also introduced natural selection as a universal law of nature. Matthew has been ignored by most scientists ever since Darwin wrote him up, in the 1872 *Historical Sketch* attached to the sixth edition of the *Origin of Species*, as someone advocating Cuvierian and Lamarckian views.

Matthew has been frequently criticised for not continuing to develop his ideas. What more could he have done? The next advance, heredity, securely founded by Mendel, was in the literature by 1865. Like Matthew's natural selection so Darwin's natural selection had no more to say and, indeed, had little influence in the nineteenth century. Darwin did not build on his ideas from 1859 because without the heredity aspect the next part of the jigsaw of transmutation could not be put in place. Darwin and his set missed Mendel's paper circulating in a European journal as well as Matthew's Appendix.

Darwin, from the moment Matthew made his protest in 1860, started to rubbish Matthew by referring to him as 'an obscure writer' and by claiming that Matthew merely enunciated the principle of natural selection. In the *Historical Sketch* for the sixth edition, Darwin finally admitted that Matthew's views were not far from his own. However, authors who have even condescended to mention Matthew have all seized on Darwin's 'merely enunciated' and continued to rubbish Matthew on that basis. These authors rarely read Darwin's works beyond the first edition of 1859, and so are ignorant of what Darwin wrote later on. One gains the impression that many devoted Darwinists are not very knowledgeable about Darwin's published works. Such authors continue to refer to Matthew as 'obscure' when, in fact, Darwin considered him important enough to be included in the *Historical Sketch*, and devoted as much space to him as was devoted to Lamarck.

So the *Origin of Species* has been regarded up to the present day as one of the greatest scientific essays of all time. Look at any essay or book on Darwin and you will find the only edition referenced is the 1859 one. Darwin's ideas matured over the years as Ospovat (1995) has clearly shown. So, why the reticence about the later editions? After 1859, Darwin added little to the *Origin of Species*. Just compare the chapter on 'Natural selection' in the first edition with what is in the third and subsequent editions. As Ospovat points out, a whole new section was added to that chapter in the third edition and that section is still there in the sixth edition. If, then, Darwinists refuse to read beyond the 1859 edition, their knowledge of the *Origin* is, *de facto*, limited.

The headings of the new section in the sixth edition are: 'On the degree to which organisation tends to advance' and 'Convergence of character'. However, the summary of the chapter remains unchanged. For Ospovat to spend so much time building up a case to support his contention that the 'branching concept' was Darwin's contribution is unfortunate. Once again Ospovat's unawareness of Patrick Matthew and Edward Blyth led him to attribute to Darwin a concept that had been confidently expressed years before.

Worldwide demand for the *Origin of Species* necessitated new editions. If one compares the first and second editions with the sixth, one finds some words have been changed, 'inherited' has been inserted in several places, a few phrases have been slightly altered, there is a bit about reversion, the conditions of life and use and disuse, together with the additions of the third and sixth editions. Why then do Darwinists confine themselves to the 1859 edition which, in any case, is extremely rare? Just recently there has been issued a reprint of the second edition. Why reprint an edition that is incomplete Darwinism? Darwin stated in the sixth edition that he had taken account of recent information, yet continued to reject catastrophes. He also added Pangenesis to the sixth edition. Although this subject is an embarrassment to devoted Darwinists, it surely is evidence of what Darwin's mature ideas amounted to. Even this idea was a rehash of the speculation of Maupertuis a century before. The fact is that Darwin and Wallace ended up with Pangenesis.

One other addition to the sixth edition is the 1872 *Historical Sketch* in its final form. In this Darwin acknowledges that Lamarck was the first to establish natural law to life of all kinds including man. This is a further embarrassment for those Darwinists who regularly criticise Lamarck and reduce his concepts to the inheritance of acquired characters.

There have been warnings not to read the sixth edition because it contains too many mistakes. By 'mistakes' is usually meant Lamarckisms that are supposed to be absent from the 1859 edition. I have not come across anyone who has pointed out that in Darwin's *The Descent of Man* (1871, 1874) there is this statement in the Preface: 'whereas, even in the first edition of the *Origin of Species*, I distinctly stated that great weight must be attributed to the inherited effects of use and disuse, with respect to both mind and body...' (note the Lamarckism). And again: '...and secondly that natural selection had been the chief agent of change aided by the inherited effects of habit, and slightly by the direct action of surrounding conditions' (note the Lamarckisms).

Modern Darwinists do not seem to be aware that support for Lamarck's inheritance of acquired characteristics is in the first edition of the *Origin of Species*. Darwin made it clear what he was about but he never attached Lamarck's name to those concepts. In spite of Darwin's previous protestations, Eldredge (1986) states that 'Darwin even allowed the inheritance of acquired characteristics to creep into his argument in the sixth edition.' And even then Eldredge omits Lamarck's name or what the concepts were, and appears to have missed Darwin's statement on use and disuse (see below).

In the preface to *The Descent of Man* Darwin countered much criticism '...whereas, even in the first edition of the *Origin of Species*, I distinctly stated that great weight must be attributed to the inherited effects of use and disuse ... I also attribute some amount of modification to the direct and prolonged action of changed conditions of life'. Far from being introduced into the sixth edition, as Eldredge (1995) suggests, Darwin had it in the very *first* edition, and said so himself. This statement is often referred to as 'Darwin's pluralistic idea', But Darwin never revealed, in the *Origin*, that these concepts derived from Lamarck. One has to turn to the *Historical Sketch* to find Lamarckian concepts detailed by Darwin.

Eldredge seems also to be unaware that in the first edition Darwin supported Lamarck's theory by rejecting 'the old notion' of catastrophes and mass extinctions.

A careful study of the *Origin of Species*, in which Lamarck is mentioned once, indicates that most Darwinists have followed Darwin in writing Lamarck out of the literature. One may wonder here why Darwin, in 1881, admitted that he had attributed too little weight to the conditions of life – unlike Patrick Matthew. Considering the number of times he refers to this Lamarckian concept in the *Origin*, it is odd that Darwin should have been so modest – or was he denying his Lamarckism?

Darwin was quite right and, indeed, quite courageous in pointing out, in *The Descent of Man*, that he had stressed the heredity aspect of use and disuse. The first sentence in both the 1859 and 1872 editions of the *Origin of Species* are similar: 'Effects of use and disuse. From the facts alluded to in the first chapter, I think there can be little doubt that use in our domestic animals strengthens and enlarges certain parts, and in disuse diminishes them; and that such modifications are inherited.' Cuvier, and later Darwin and Wallace, ridiculed Lamarck whose concept this was. So those, like Richard Dawkins, who consider the 1859 edition to be free of 'mistakes' are themselves mistaken.

So, why at the end of his life, did Darwin openly praise and acknowledge Lamarck's priority, when for 30 years he had ridiculed him? A possible explanation is that Darwin originally wrote the *Origin of Species* as a covert Lamarckian and now, because Lyell had recanted and gone on to support Lamarck since 1863, he became an overt Lamarckian. Little wonder that Darwinists do not want people to read the sixth edition. There is, however, a Lamarckism, 'the conditions of life', on page 1 of Chapter 1 of the 1859 edition, without any reference to Lamarck!

We must come now to discuss what was original in the *Origin of Species*. One can assess the claim of originality by discussing the main concepts in the book.

The importance of varieties

The first sentence reveals the subject that Darwin was really interested in: 'When we look to the individuals of the same variety or sub-variety of our older domesticated plants and animals, one of the first points which strikes us is that they generally differ more from each other than do the individuals of any one species or variety in a state of nature'. This was a well-known observation, and John Hunter (1728–93), the Scottish surgeon and naturalist, was aware of it. In his *Essays and Observations* of 1861, Hunter remarks that:

> These different breeds of the same species, although they be pretty constant in their heredity properties, and by getting the breed we are pretty sure of the produce, yet they are often varying from the true breed: but, these are either better or worse than the original: but, whichever it may be, it in some degree becomes an hereditary principle.
>
> The varieties among the original of any one species of animals are much less than the varieties of any one species. Thus the wolves have less varieties among themselves than we find in any of the varieties of dogs; whether we take the bull-dog, mastiff, greyhound etc. The same may be observed of Man.

We know, from his notebooks, that Darwin had read the unpublished essays of Hunter, which were stored in the Hunterian Museum, where Richard Owen identified the fossils sent home from the *Beagle*. We know also that Darwin had a great respect for Hunter and it may be that Darwin noticed Hunter's comments on varieties.

Patrick Matthew (1831) had also observed that domestic varieties were more numerous than species in the wild, and provided a possible explanation for this state of affairs: 'Man's interference, by preventing this natural process of selection among plants, independent of the wider range of circumstances to which he introduces them, has increased the difference in varieties, particularly in the more domesticated kinds.' Matthew also proposed another aspect of natural selection: '...those only come forward to maturity from the strict ordeal by which Nature tests their adaptation to Her standard of perfection and fitness to continue their kind of reproduction'.

Gould (2002) reminds us that everyone was agreed about Matthew's second statement: that is regarded as the negative aspect of natural selection. Gould continues:

131

Darwin's theory therefore cannot be equated with the simple claim that natural selection operates ... Darwin, in his characteristic and radical way, grasped that the standard mechanism for preserving the type could be inverted, and then converted into the primary cause of evolutionary change ... but we must recognise, as Darwin's second key postulates, the claim that natural selection acts as the creative force of evolutionary change. The essence of Darwinism cannot reside in the mere observation that natural selection operates – for everyone had long accepted a negative side for natural selection in eliminating the unfit and preserving the type.

Had Gould read Matthew's book and Appendix he would have found that Matthew was well aware of the creative aspect of natural selection and said so in the above first statement which, it is claimed, is the first occasion that natural selection occurred in print. And Darwin did not miss that point in averring that Matthew 'Saw, clearly the full force of the principle of natural selection'.

Mutation of species

This was the basis of the bitter disagreement between Cuvier and Lamarck and Cuvier and St Hilaire in the first three decades of the nineteenth century. Cuvier believed that species were miraculously created and were fixed, as Linnaeus concluded in the eighteenth century. Lamarck, as Darwin pointed out in the *Descent of Man*, argued on the basis of his evidence that evolution was a fact and species mutated. If you believe species mutate, then *ipso facto* you accept evolution. In 1844, Darwin wrote to Joseph Hooker to say he now agreed with Lamarck that species mutated. This was a break from the view of his mentor, Charles Lyell, but this fact was not put in the *Origin of Species*. What Darwin confessed to Hooker was never included in any edition of the *Origin*.

Descent from a common ancestor

Lamarck introduced this concept in 1809. Matthew has it in his Appendix of 1831, Edward Blyth has it in his 1835–7 essays (but

132

rejected it as contrary to Holy Writ), and Lyell has it in his *Principles of Geology*, Volume 2 (1832) (though he rejected it as contrary to Christian theology). It is not clear when Darwin accepted this concept but it must have been after 1844. There is nothing in the *Origin of Species* relating this concept to Lamarck.

Natural selection

Patrick Matthew first introduced this concept as a universal law of nature and never changed his mind about its supreme importance. In *The Descent of Man*, Darwin stated that he had attributed too much to natural selection in the early editions of the *Origin of Species*. It is impossible to make out what passages he had in mind because the text is little changed in the sixth edition. In the *Historical Sketch*, Darwin grudgingly admitted that Matthew 'saw clearly the full force of the principle of natural selection' but refrained from admitting that he was the first to introduce the concept. One has constantly to check just what Darwin has written in all his publications. In the *Historical Sketch*, for example, on one page is this statement: 'As far as mere enunciation of the principle of natural selection is concerned, it is quite immaterial whether or not Professor Owen preceded me, for both of us, as shown in the *Historical Sketch*, were long ago preceded by Dr Wells and Mr Matthews.' Darwin did not even get the latter's name right!

On the preceding page is this statement: 'The differences of Mr Matthew's view from mine are not of much importance.' So much for 'mere enunciation', but this stuck and Darwinists always quote this phrase when degrading Matthew. But the differences between Darwin's and Matthew's views were important because, as Darwin continues, 'he seems to consider the world was nearly depopulated on successive occasions and then restocked'. Darwin did not believe this, because Uniformitarianism had got rid of Cuvier's catastrophes. Darwin then continues, 'but it seems that he attributes much influence to the direct action of the conditions of life'.

What is the casual reader to make of that? Darwin did not invite his readers to look up page 1, Chapter 1, in all editions of the *Origin of Species* to find the first enunciation of 'the conditions of life' without any reference to Lamarck. 'The conditions of life', as

I have pointed out numerous times thus far, was Darwin's translation of Lamarck's 'circumstances'.

History of the earth

Darwin accepted *in toto* Lyell's Uniformitarianism and so dispensed with catastrophes, Ice Ages and mass extinctions followed by periods of apparent rapid speciation, followed by stability of the species for millions of years. Under the influence of Lyell's Uniformitarianism Darwin rejected any role for catastrophes in the history of the earth and even that they had ever occurred. In the section on Extinction (Chapter 10, 1859 edition, and Chapter 11, 1872 edition) is the following: 'The old notion of all inhabitants of the earth having been swept away at successive periods by catastrophes, is very generally given up, even by those geologists ... whose views would naturally lead them to this conclusion.'

So far as Lyell's religious views were concerned, the Newtonian equilibrium had to be maintained. Why Darwin made no protest about this indicates how deeply he was enthralled by Lyell's Uniformitarianism. Perhaps the real reason was Darwin's extraordinary antipathy to Cuvier.

Divergence

Darwin wrote to Lyell, while he was writing the *Origin* in 1859, saying that he had taken a very long time to understand divergence. Ospovat's (1995) examination of what Darwin was thinking about during the years from 1847 to 1856 bears this out. It is possible that Wallace's 1855 essay, which discussed divergence, may have concentrated Darwin's mind, although he told Lyell he found nothing new in that essay. Cuvier introduced divergence with the four main branches of animal life. Lamarck added collaterals because Cuvier did not recognise any heredity link along the linear series. Matthew, in 1831, added 'diverging ramifications' and Blyth (1835–7) 'reiterate diversity'. Darwin probably picked up divergence from Blyth and in his notes of 1837 depicted a tree of life. Darwin sent a copy of the 1859 edition of the *Origin of Species* to his friend Asa Gray at Harvard. When Gray came to the conclusion that organisms can breed true but can also diverge and pass the variation to the progeny, he wrote in the margin 'and so it comes to Lamarck after all' (Dupree 1959). Darwin makes no mention, in the *Origin of Species*, of Cuvier as the founder of divergence or Cuvier as the discoverer of catastrophes. Darwin's principle of divergence is presented by Ospovat without any reference to previous authors.

What Patrick Matthew referred to as 'diverging ramifications' in 1831, Ospovat calls 'the branching conception' of Darwin:

> With its extension to palaeontology around 1850, the branching conception informed work in all the most important disciplines in natural history, except geographical distribution for which it had no very direct significance ... the natural history of the mid-nineteenth century was in consequence very different from that of Cuvier or the British naturalists of the period 1800–1830.

So Patrick Matthew, writing his book in the 1820s, is the first British naturalist to develop Lamarck's 'collaterals' or embranchments, which linked genetically the animals along the Cuvier branches. Edward Blyth was not far behind with 'reiterate diversity' in 1835–7. These naturalists were aware of the so-called branching concept long before the discovery of a wealth of fossil material towards the mid-nineteenth century, which made branching obvious – or more obvious. Even Henri Milne-Edwards did not get around to the concept until about 1844 and Darwin was greatly influenced by his essay on the division of labour.

Man's place in nature

There was nothing about man's place in nature in any edition of the *Origin of Species*, but the subject does appear in *The Descent of Man*. He confessed in the Preface that he had introduced nothing original in his book and that Lamarck had long ago concluded that man was of simian origin. Darwin now accepted Lamarck's concept and this represented another break from his mentor, Charles Lyell.

The heredity link to use and disuse and change of habits

In 1863, after three editions of the *Origin of Species* had been published, Lyell wrote to Darwin to say that he could see no difference between Darwinism and Lamarckism. Considering the lengths to which Lyell went to get the *Origin* published, his change of mind is not easy to understand without a detailed study of what Lamarck had written. Darwin was not entirely honest in his reply to Lyell's letter because, for the second time, he denied that he had got anything of importance from Lamarck's book. Here is Darwin's comment about it: '[it is] what I consider, after two deliberate readings ... a wretched book, and one from which (I well remember my surprise) I gained nothing'. (F. Darwin)

Lyell's 1863 letter to Darwin came after 30 years of degrading Lamarck. Lyell, for some strange reason, became a Lamarckian. He was no less pious than he was in 1832 but now he had second thoughts. On 15 March 1863, he wrote to Darwin the following: 'when I came to the conclusion that after all Lamarck was going to be shown to be right, that we must "go the whole oran" I re-read his book, and remembering when it was written, I felt I had done him an injustice'. Having reread Lamarck's work, Lyell realised that there was no difference between Lamarckism and Darwinism, and he wrote to Darwin to say so. That letter forced Darwin to be more honest about his sources and Lamarck's concepts, now listed in the *Historical Sketch* but not in the *Origin of Species*. This led Romanes (1893) to conclude that Darwin had never been influenced by Lamarck's speculations.

Although Darwin denied, in his letters, that Lamarck was of any importance, he distinctly stressed the importance of Lamarckian concepts. He went out of his way to insert 'inherited' in the sixth edition of the *Origin*, when this operative word was missing in earlier editions. For example, 'Habit also has a decided influence, as in the period of flowering plants when transported from one climate to another (*Origin of Species* 1859) became, in the 1872 edition, 'Changed habits produce an inherited effect, as in the period of the flowering plants when transported from one climate to another.'

In the final form of the *Historical Sketch*, Darwin states some of Lamarck's concepts:

In these works he upholds the doctrine that all species, including man, are descended from other species. He first did the eminent service of arousing attention to the probability of all change in the organic, as well as the inorganic, world being the result of law, and not of miraculous interposition. Lamarck seems to have been chiefly led to his conclusion on the gradual change in species by the difficulty of distinguishing species and varieties, by the almost perfect gradation of forms in certain groups, and by the analogy of domestic productions. With respect to the means of modification, he attributed something to the crossing of already existing forms, and much to use and disuse, that is, to the effects of habit.

But this was not all that Lamarck had written about. Darwin admitted, in a letter to Hooker in 1844, that he now agreed with Lamarck that species mutated. Another Lamarckian concept was descent from a common ancestor, and the struggle for existence was yet another. Darwin uses the concept to explain what Matthew had described as the 'steady state': 'As long as the conditions of life remain the same, we have reason to believe that a modification, which has already been inherited for many generations, may continue to be inherited for an almost infinite number of generations.' Matthew was also of this opinion. Reading the above and other Lamarckian concepts in the *Origin*, no wonder Charles Lyell could see no difference between Lamarckism and Darwinism.

In 1860 Darwin wrote to Professor Baden-Powell: 'The only novelty in my work is the attempt to explain how species became modified and to a certain extent how the theory of descent explains large classes of facts; in this respect I received no assistance from my predecessors.' This is debatable and Darwin only managed to get away with it because he refused to give his sources, which it turns out, were mainly Lamarckian.

If we turn to another statement included in Darwin's list of what constituted Lamarckism we find: 'and by the analogy of domestic productions'. Darwin stressed this concept on several occasions: 'There is no reason why the principles which have acted so efficiently under domestication should not have acted in nature.' But Wallace's essay of 1858 claimed that this was all false and this shows that Wallace did not really understand natural selection. So, in the first and, indeed, in all later editions of the *Origin*, Darwin ridiculed

Wallace's assertion: 'I have in vain endeavoured to discover on what decisive facts the above statement has so often and so boldly made. There would be great difficulty in proving its truth...' Darwin's full statement in this respect can be found on page 467.

On receiving Wallace's 1858 essay, Darwin immediately sent it on to Lyell with an attached letter: 'We differ only [in] that I was led to my views from what artificial selection has done for domestic animals.' This, again, is Lamarckism, which had been repeated by Naudin in a paper of 1852 and sent to Darwin by Hooker.

Among Darwin's list of Lamarckian concepts is 'the conditions of life'. On the first page of the 1859 edition of the *Origin* is this sentence: 'it seems pretty clear that organic beings must be exposed during several generations to the new conditions of life to cause any appreciable amount of variation'. No mention of Lamarck. In the very last chapter of the *Origin* is this: 'Man does not actually produce variability, he only unintentionally exposes organic beings to new conditions of life, and then nature acts on the organisation, and causes variability'. Why, then, did Darwin write to Professor Semper in 1881 to say that he had not attributed sufficient weight to 'the conditions of life'? In the *Historical Sketch* (1872) Darwin pointed out that Patrick Matthew attributed great weight to the conditions of life without making it clear whether he agreed or not. In that same letter to Professor Semper, Darwin continues 'but Hoffman's paper has staggered me. Perhaps hundreds of generations are necessary. It is a most perplexing subject'.

Darwinists are now stressing that Darwin's overriding significance, even if he was anticipated by Matthew, was his impact factor. But the evolutionary impact factor was established in France in the early decades of the nineteenth century. As we have seen in earlier chapters, the impact in France was lessened in England by the series of Seditious Acts and by the suppression of so-called atheistic French science. By the time Lyell came to realise that the *Origin*, from start to finish, was Lamarckism together with the speculation of natural selection, Darwinism had begun, and continues, to dominate the scientific world.

Reversion

Variation under domestication (1859 and 1872 editions):

having alluded to the subject of reversion, I may here refer to a statement often made by naturalists – namely, that our domestic varieties, when run wild, gradually but certainly revert in character to their aboriginal stocks. Hence it has been argued that no deductions can be drawn from domestic races to species in a state of nature. I have in vain endeavoured to discover on what decisive facts the above statement has so often and so boldly made. There would be great difficulty in proving its truth...

As we have seen, in another section of the *Origin of Species* Darwin claimed: 'There is no obvious reason why the principles which have acted so efficiently under domestication should not have acted under nature.' It is clear from these statements that Darwin had been won over to Lamarck. Indeed, he reveals this himself in the *Historical Sketch*. If one recalls Darwin's immediate reaction to Wallace's 1858 essay it was on the domestic production basis that he differed from Wallace. This evidence seems to indicate that Darwin was a covert Lamarckian from the beginning and in his old age was quite overt.

Darwin, as we know, owed a great deal to Blyth's 1835–7 essays, but never betrayed the fact. The conclusion to Alfred Wallace's 1858 essay, which he sent to Darwin with a request for its onward transmission to Charles Lyell, is the direct opposite to the above statement:

It will be observed that this argument rests entirely on the assumption that varieties occurring in the state of nature are in all respects analogous to and even identical with those of domestic animals, and are governed by the same laws as regards their permanence or further variation. But it is the object of this paper to show that this assumption is altogether false...

In spite of this conclusion to an essay that did not include the actual words 'natural selection' but was *about the principle of* natural selection, Darwin accepted it as an anticipation of his own ideas of evolution by natural selection. Why? Darwin got most of his ideas from Blyth and so did Wallace. It would seem that Darwin was prepared to accept Wallace in order to cover up his own dependence on Blyth. At first Wallace argued *against* natural selection in favour of survival of the fittest, but there is no evidence that he continued his disagreement. According to McKinney (1972), Wallace read and annotated Blyth's essays in the *Magazine of Natural History*. These are the essays of 1835–7 that influenced Darwin in writing the *Origin*, and it would seem that Darwin accepted Wallace's 1858 essay but quickly appealed to Lyell and Hooker for help. McKinney continues: 'Nevertheless, he also examined his notes on Blyth's paper of 1835 and in his famous paper of 1858 probably quoted from these notes in one or two places.' This is an extraordinary observation to make without rereading Blyth's articles and Wallace's essay in order to check the degree of alleged plagiarism. In fact, McKinney fails to make a convincing argument because any casual reader would not realise from his vague remarks what the extent of apparent plagiarism really was. My assessment (Dempster 1996), based on documentary evidence, was that almost half of the essay was taken from Blyth's work.

McKinney (1972) spends several pages in order to expose Wallace's deception about where he wrote his 1858 essay – Ternate or Gilolo (see Chapter 3). He then asks the question, 'Why did Wallace carry out such a deception?' His response is that 'the picture of Wallace that seems to emerge from this curious incident is that of a somewhat romantic scientist, with a definite flair for a colourful story'.

McKinney appears not to be acquainted with Darwin's long struggle with divergence. Ospovat (1995) is quite confident that Darwin was gathering information about divergence between 1854 and 1857. On the evidence of Darwin's notebooks, Ospovat states that 'the principle of divergence was invented in the summer of 1857'. Did Wallace's 1855 essay have any influence on the invention? So, the long tortuous discussion on the principle in Chapters 4 and 13 of the *Origin* took to 12 June 1859. It is unhelpful, then to accuse Darwin of plagiarising Wallace's 1858 essay without firm evidence.

In his notebook of 1837 Darwin introduced a branching tree, which he seems to have forgotten for 20 years. There is no mention of it in the 1842 or 1844 essays. Diversity first appears in the extract read out at the Linnean Society in 1858.

Considering how quickly Patrick Matthew and Edward Blyth recognised and understood the importance of Cuvier's divergence and Lamarck's collaterals, it would seem that Darwin was right to confess to Lyell that it had taken him a long time to understand divergence. How Darwin could ponder a law of descent and natural selection without first understanding divergence is odd.

Although aware of Lamarck's embranchements but always unaware of Matthew and Blyth, Ospovat (1995) attributes the branching business to Darwin:

> Darwin's discussions of constancy are closely bound up with his discussions of one of the principle features of his evolutionary system – branching, the multiplication of species. From a very early stage in his speculations Darwin assumed that evolution is a branching, rather than a linear process.

From an early age Darwin had been introduced to Lamarck. It is a pity Ospovat had not been introduced to Patrick Matthew's statement describing the after-events of a catastrophe: 'destroying all living things, must have reduced existence so much, that an unoccupied field would be formed for new diverging ramifications of life.' Surely here is branching and the multiplication of species.

In 1856 Darwin took on board Milne-Edwards' 'division of labour' concept. It was this concept that Ospovat claims 'was largely responsible for the transformation of the theory of natural selection between 1844 and 1859'. In the *Origin*, Darwin actually named Milne-Edwards as his source and confidently concluded that 'Natural selection, as has been remarked, leads to divergence of character and to much extinction of the less improved and intermediate forms of life'. Here is Matthew on the same theme: 'The unremitting operation of this law ... by careful selection of the largest or most valuable as breeders ... only the hardier, most robust, better suited to circumstances, who are able to struggle forward to maturity...'

Although one must admire Ospovat's patient tracing of what he calls Darwin's branching theory, he has apparently not taken into account what Matthew had written many years before. It took a long time for Darwin to realise that Milne-Edwards' division of labour theory had 'The unmistakable message ... that divergence is a general feature of nature.' Matthew was well aware of this, as demonstrated by his confident, perhaps arrogant, matter of fact observations written in the 1820s.

Of course writers, over the decades, accepted Wallace as a co-founder of evolution, which indicates that Wallace's 1858 essay and the Darwin correspondence about the profound disagreement has never been carefully analysed. Darwin spotted the difference in Wallace's assertion and said so in his letter to Lyell accompanying the essay that was sent off the very day he received it (18 June). An unseemly episode – 'the delicate situation' – then followed which involved Hooker and Lyell misleading the secretary of the Linnean Society into allowing a joint reading of Darwin's extracts and Wallace's essay within 14 days of the essay supposedly arriving at Darwin's home.

I have stated above that Darwin received Wallace's 1858 essay on 18 June. McKinney (1972) has suggested that the date was 3 June because letters sent from Ternate on the same date arrived at Frederick and Henry Bates on 3 June. The inference McKinney draws is that during the period 3 to 18 June Darwin took over Wallace's idea of divergence. What McKinney and others have missed is that there was more about divergence in the 1855 essay than in the 1858 essay. Furthermore, Dupree (1959) states that Darwin started on divergence on 14 April 1859 and finished it on 12 June.

Wallace even got his criticism of Lamarck wrong. He followed the usual misinterpretation about the giraffe's neck: 'Neither did the giraffe acquire its long neck by desiring to reach the foliage of the more lofty shrubs, and constantly stretching its neck for the purpose...' This was not what Lamarck had written. Rather, he said that the giraffe

> is forced to reach upwards continually. This habit, indulged in for a long time by all the individuals of the race, has resulted in lengthening the fore-legs more than the hind legs, and has so elongated the neck that the giraffe, without rising on its hind legs, elevates its head and reaches upwards six metres, or almost twenty feet.

Darwin took Lamarck's concept for his own purposes. In the Introduction to *The Descent of Man* Darwin stated:

> nor must we forget what I have called 'Correlated' growth, meaning thereby, that various parts of the organisation are in some unknown manner so connected, that when one part varies, so do others; and if variations in the one are accumulated by selection, other parts will be modified.

No mention of Lamarck. Yet Lamarck had observed that any major structural change in an animal initiated structural change elsewhere. Cuvier also was concerned with correlate growth.

Considering that Darwin must have known that Cuvier had introduced divergence, and that Lamarck had added to it the heredity link which Cuvier denied, and Matthew and Blyth had added 'diverging ramifications' and 'reiterate diversity' it was a miserable piece Darwin inserted in his abstract for the Linnean Society meeting and later in the *Origin*. This indicates Darwin never had a good grasp of the fundamental significance of the phenomenon of divergence. In all six editions of the *Origin of Species* Darwin never mentioned Cuvier's four main branches of animal life that are the starting point of the phenomenon of divergence. That Darwin took divergence from Wallace is nonsense, but in omitting Cuvier's fundamental contribution he left himself open to this assertion. I cannot find any criticism of Darwin's omission of Cuvier's great contribution to and founding of vertebrate palaeontology.

Conditions of life (Lamarck) and conditions of existence (Cuvier)

Darwin confessed in a letter in 1881 that he had never given sufficient attention to the above conditions. This led him to discuss natural selection inadequately in several parts of the *Origin*. Take, for instance, Darwin's remarks about the eyes of moles. Not fully understanding Lamarck's concept that the conditions of life had to be considered in any structural change any animal may resort to, he became bogged down in confusion. Any change would be determined by the conditions of life. The ability to naturally select these conditions would determine whether the animal survived or not. Then having reached a stage of 'circumstance-suited' (Matthew's phrase) the species would remain in a 'steady' state (Matthew's word) for millions of years. In the *Historical Sketch* Darwin pointed out that Matthew laid emphasis on the importance of the conditions of life but in a way which gave the impression that he (Darwin) did not agree. The concept was Lamarckian, hence heretical and scientifically incorrect.

But Darwin claimed that he had a reason for not taking seriously 'the conditions of life'. He explained to Moritz Wagner in 1872 that:

When I wrote the *Origin*, and for some years afterwards, I could find little evidence of the direct action of the environment, now there is a large body of evidence, and your case of the Saturn is one of the most remarkable of which I have heard.

Is it not odd that there seemed to be enough evidence by the time Darwin was a child to satisfy Lamarck and Cuvier and enough evidence later on to satisfy Patrick Matthew and Edward Blyth? Huxley then wrote Darwin, 'it is not clear to me why, if continued physical conditions are of so little moment as you suppose, variation should occur at all'. All this is rather confusing if one is aware that the phrase 'conditions of life' is to be found on the very first page of the *Origin* of 1859 and at various intervals all through that and other editions.

It was as late as 1872 before Darwin detailed some of Lamarck's concepts in the *Historical Sketch* incorporated in the sixth edition of the *Origin of Species*. Most of the concepts were employed by Darwin in writing the *Origin* but without mentioning Lamarck's name. When Asa Gray received a copy of the 1859 edition he recognised immediately the extent of Lamarck's concepts in the *Origin*. Having read his copy of the 1859 edition he wrote on the book, 'so it comes to Lamarck after all'. Although Gray did a great deal in America to spread Darwinism, he never went so far as Darwin in accepting the inheritance of acquired characteristics (Dupree 1959). Darwin became so absorbed in Lamarckism that he spent some time in working on what he called Pangenesis. In introducing this concept, Darwin imagined he had found a mechanism to explain the perplexing problem of how acquired characteristics could be inherited. It would seem that Gray supported Darwinism as one way of countering the influence of Agassiz. These two had no time for one another. But Gray was not the only naturalist to recognise the extent of Lamarckism in the *Origin of Species*. Among the first reviewers of the first edition were H.G. Bronn and Francois Pictet, who commented right away that Lamarck's *Philosophy of Zoology* had been revived (Hull 1973).

Here are some examples of Lamarckian concepts incorporated into the *Origin of Species*: mutation of species; inheritance of acquired characteristics; conditions of life; speciation over immense time; descent from a common ancestor; the distinction between real affinities and analogical resemblances; the importance of domestic productions. Of these only the last one stimulated Darwin to consider natural selection. Darwin acknowledged in the *Origin* the distinction noted above and this was probably because other authors had noticed and commented on Lamarck's distinction, especially Darwin's contemporary, Macleay. Perhaps Darwin felt that Macleay was passing off this concept as his own.

Darwin acknowledged in *The Descent of Man* that man is a class of mammal, derived from lower species. In his introduction to that book, Darwin stated: 'In conclusion that man is the descendent with other species of ancient, lower extinct forms is not in any degree new. Lamarck long ago came to the same conclusion which has lately been maintained by several eminent naturalists and philosophers.' That said, consider this: 'Almost seventy-six years ago – February 24, 1871, to be exact – Darwin published *The Descent of Man*, and so laid the foundation of our modern knowledge of man's origin' (Keith 1949).

In *A New Theory of Human Evolution* Keith, like Darwin, mentions Lamarck once only, to say that nobody believes his concepts. Except, that is, his famous pupil and eminent anthropologist, Wood Jones, 'Who regards the many adaptations of the human body as a result of use and wont'. Another example of a devoted Darwinist ignoring what Darwin had admitted.

In four years spent close to Sir Arthur Keith I never heard him mention Lamarck's name. When Keith looked at Darwin he could see a halo above his head. The only complaint Keith seemed to have about Darwin was, 'Why did Darwin cold-shoulder Herbert Spencer?' Like so many Darwin enthusiasts he never understood Darwin's true character and failed to pay sufficient attention to what Darwin wrote after 1868.

By 1905 Darwinism had to be changed to neo-Darwinism in order to remove Pangenesis from Darwinism. That term survived unopposed until the recent crisis in Darwinism when one author, involved in the crisis, wished to change once again and reinvent Darwin (Eldredge 1995). The crisis developed because some naturalists are of the opinion that speciation can, at some periods, be rapid. Darwin stubbornly refused to countenance this when Thomas Huxley tried to convince him of it. Right up to the 1872 edition of the *Origin* Darwin maintained that 'If we look to long enough intervals of time, geology plainly declares that species have all changed; and they have changed in the manner required by the

145

theory, for they have changed slowly and in a gradual manner.' And further: 'Why should not Nature take a sudden leap, from structure to structure? On the theory of natural selection, we can clearly understand why She should not, for natural selection acts only by taking advantage of slight successive variations; she can never take a great leap, but must advance by short and sure, although slow steps.' This is Lamarckism.

Another group of naturalists maintain, in spite of Darwin's statements to the contrary, that Darwinism embraces both rapid *and* slow speciation. It would appear that this group are trying to defend a defenceless position; a position that Darwin himself would not defend. Darwin stated quite clearly in every edition of the *Origin* that catastrophes and mass extinctions had been 'given up'; even invented. This was in accord with Lyell's Uniformitarianism that dismissed catastrophes and mass extinctions. It was after periods of mass extinction that periods of rapid speciation are believed to have occurred. This belief is based on the geological and palaeontological data. Punctuated equilibrium, which involves periods of rapid speciation following catastrophes and mass extinctions, is not a Darwinian concept.

Was it the intention of Lyell and Darwin to leave behind them such a confused state? Lyell certainly made his position clear in the twelfth edition of his *Principles* (1875). If we can accept the word of George Romanes, the psychologist, who was close to Darwin in his last years, Darwin lost confidence in natural selection as the most important factor in evolution and was more and more going over to Lamarckian concepts. In about 1875 George Romanes came into Darwin's life. Boakes (1984) considers that Romanes got the impression that, late in his life, Darwin was attributing more importance to Lamarckian inheritance as a means of accelerating evolution than when he had written the *Origin of Species*. But as we know, a careful reading of the *Origin* reveals that Darwin was following Lamarck from the very beginning. One tends to be influenced by Darwin's young friend into thinking that Darwin veered towards Lamarckism over the years. But I have indicated here that by 1863 Lyell realised how much Lamarckism was in Darwinism.

Darwin certainly did a great service in bringing together in one volume a vast amount of the scientific information of his day. However, there is nothing original. From start to finish what is called Darwinism is Lamarckism. The confusion was caused by Darwin's apparent refusal to give his sources. His repeated statements confirming his support for the inheritance of acquired characteristics were the stimuli which drove him to his version of the theory of Pangenesis. Why did Darwin spend so much time trying to find a theory which would prove the truth of the inheritance of acquired characteristics? While privately ridiculing the subject, Darwin could not get it out of his mind. His repeated support for the subject in the *Origin of Species* seems to have gone unnoticed by most people. When Huxley pointed out to Darwin that Pangenesis was in Buffon's published works Darwin said he was ashamed of his theory but never withdrew it. His close allegiance to his mentor, Charles Lyell, however, meant that he discarded the very basis of the earth's past history. Out went Cuvier's catastrophes, mass extinctions and the rapid speciation that followed. Darwin never betrayed the slightest hint that Cuvier had introduced divergence with the four main branches of animal life.

If all Darwinists were as widely read and as honest as Ospovat I would not have to be defending Cuvier and Lamarck. Ospovat, who died tragically at a young age, states quite clearly that the founders of the history of the earth were Lamarck and Cuvier.

Although Ospovat's book was first published in 1981 and has been much praised by Darwinists, I find that little critical attention has been paid to what is actually in the book. While reading it, one is constantly made aware that Ospovat is very conscious of the basic contributions of Cuvier and Lamarck. One comes across statements such as this:

> Macleay credited Cuvier, along with Lamarck, with founding the modern study of zoology. But while Cuvier was undoubtedly the best comparative anatomist in the world, his efforts to find the natural system were, in Macleay's opinion, far inferior to those of Lamarck.

Ospovat, however, failed to point out that Darwin never admitted this: Macleay did not approve of Lamarck's theory of transmutation'. Not only Macleay, but everyone else among Darwin's contemporaries.

Macleay, as we know, was a contemporary of Darwin. Why then did Darwin not admit what Macleay admitted? We come back to Darwin's refusal to give his sources. If Ospovat could state the

147

historical fact, why is it rare to find in essays on Darwinism that Cuvier or Lamarck are mentioned? The most obvious answer is because Darwin only once, in the *Origin of Species*, introduced Lamarck, and that was only because Macleay had paid great attention to a particular Lamarckian concept. Cuvier is mentioned twice – on one occasion to point out that Cuvier had got the age of a class of fossil wrong and this was because the geological data were found after Cuvier's death; the other occasion concerned conditions of existence.

Gould and Eldredge are convinced that Darwin was wrong about slow gradual change. Indeed Thomas Huxley tried, in vain, to persuade Darwin that there could be periods of rapid change. These two naturalists use the term 'stasis' to indicate the lack of structural change in species in their lifetimes. Eldredge (1986) points out that naturalists were aware, as was Darwin, that species were stable in their lifetimes. Eldredge continues:

> But stasis was conveniently dropped as a feature of life's history to be reckoned with in evolutionary biology. And stasis had continued to be ignored until Gould and I showed that stability is a real aspect of life's history which must be confronted ... it posed no fundamental threat to the basic notion of evolution itself ... Darwin felt he had to undermine the older (and ultimately biblically based) doctrine of species fixity.

But Lamarck had already done that. The biblical doctrine was opposed to transmutation of species as a concept in itself. It was Lamarck's total materialistic and atheistic attitude that so horrified the pious Charles Lyell back in 1832.

Lyell's Uniformitarianism rejected Cuvier's catastrophes and mass extinctions and consequently the periods of rapid speciation that followed. In his *Journal of Researches* (1839, 1845) Darwin claimed catastrophes were 'invented', and, as we have seen, lost no time in ruling out catastrophes from the first edition of the *Origin of Species*. If, however, one accepts that there could have been periods of the abrupt appearance of species and abrupt extinction together with the contention that species, in their lifetime, do not undergo structural change, then Gould and Eldredge have sounded the death-knell of the Lyell-Darwin evolutionary paradigm.

Ospovat (1995) goes further:

Evolution does not have to be conceived as a development from generalised archetypal forms to modern evolutionary synthesis ... But [in] Lamarck's attempt at a natural arrangement of the invertebrates Macleay saw the first, though still distant, glimpse of the system he himself revealed more fully in his *Horae Entomologicae*.

Ospovat makes the claim that Darwin was a mutationist by 1837. After five years at university and as many roving round the world, it might be expected that he had become a mutationist. But was he a mutationist by 1837? If he was, how can we explain his letter to Hooker in 1844? 'At last gleams of light have come ... I am almost convinced (quite contrary to the opinion I started with) [that] species are not immutable.' 'At last' means *now*, in 1844, and 'the opinion I started with', let us say, 1837. 'Almost convinced' is hardly the status of a mutationist of seven years' standing. Darwin even mentions in that letter that he now agrees with Lamarck! If he was a mutationist by 1837 how is it that he took so long to get to grips with divergence?

There is another piece of evidence, which throws some doubt on the suggestion that Darwin was a mutationist by 1837. The 1855 essay of Wallace reached India and was soon spotted by Edward Blyth. He wrote to Darwin warning him about this essay and ended his letter, 'Has it at all unsettled your ideas regarding the persistence of species?' Blyth had left England in 1842 and clearly had the impression at that time that Darwin was *not* a mutationist.

It will be profitable to assess Ospovat's (1995) observations:

- Ospovat had not come across Matthew's Appendix with its stress on natural laws. Darwin in his notebooks attributes laws to the Creator.
- Ospovat had not read Lyell's twelfth edition of his *Principles* and apparently had not noticed that Lyell could not find any difference between Darwinism and Lamarckism in the *Origin of Species*.
- Darwin's belief in harmony and perfect adaptation was because he, like Lyell, had dispensed with catastrophes and

mass extinctions. Ospovat asserts that 'The laws having been established by God, their consequences must be in harmony and perfection. Of this, Darwin had no doubt'. No wonder the title of Ospovat's book is *The Development of Darwin's Theory*!

- Not having read Matthew's Appendix, Ospovat confidently wrote, 'Descent was an old idea; natural selection was the novelty in Darwin's book.' Even this was an old idea. In this way Darwin's originality is perpetuated by well meaning authors who are unaware of what has already been published. Ospovat had clearly never read the 1872 *Historical Sketch* or had not adequately absorbed what Darwin had included in it.

- In discussing Darwin and his contemporaries, Ospovat appears to believe that professional biologists rather than breeders were important in the development of theory. If this were so, why was *The Cottage Gardener* Darwin's favourite journal? Why would Darwin advise Huxley that he found going to agricultural shows helpful?

- As a further development of this subject one has to note Ospovat's attention to Darwin's 'principle of divergence.' Ospovat claims that this principle grew out of Darwin's work on classification. Although Ospovat indicates that he was aware of Cuvier, I do not think he was aware that Cuvier had introduced divergence devoid of ramifications and that Lamarck had added 'collaterals.' Not having read Blyth's essays and Matthew's Appendix, it would seem that Ospovat thought Darwin introduced divergence. This is another of the many instances where concepts are attributed to Darwin but originated elsewhere.

- Ospovat indicates that most naturalists were aware that Cuvier had introduced the four main branches of animal life: 'Von Baer argued persuasively that each of Cuvier's embranchements has a different archetype'. However, Darwin never mentioned them in the *Origin of Species* although Ospovat points out that Darwin had studied the Geoffroy (St Hilaire)-Cuvier debate. In the 20 pages Ospovat devotes to this subject Cuvier is not mentioned once. In the *Origin*, Cuvier is not mentioned either, but there are now 'beautiful ramifications'. The adjective is ridiculous, though Matthew's

150

'diverging ramifications' may have been the source. Is there any other naturalist using 'diverging ramifications' besides Matthew in 1831? Ospovat confirmed that the only novelty in the *Origin* was natural selection. Although this subject had been published 30 years before, it was not tracked down by Ospovat, in spite of Darwin's admission in the *Gardener's Chronicle* of 1860 and in his letters to Patrick Matthew. If natural selection was the only novelty, why did Ospovat present Darwin's principle of divergence as if it too were a novelty?

- Then there is the quinary problem that caused Darwin so much worry. By the mid-1840s Owen and others rejected quinarism. Darwin had a great respect for Edward Blyth so who is to know why Darwin also abruptly abandoned the quinary principle with the others in 1843? Had he read Blyth on the subject? I suspect he had. Here is what Blyth had to say: 'The more deeply, indeed, I consider the quinary theory (now advocated by so many talented naturalists) in all its bearings, the less consistent does it appear to me with reason and common sense; the more thoroughly am I convinced of its utter fancifulness and misleading tendency.' Blyth had given his reasons for rejection and warned, 'Ponder this well; and it is clear, that on these grounds alone all quinary imaginings fall at once to the ground.' All this is in Blyth's 1835–37 essays which Darwin read, according to Barrett *et al.* 1987.

- In contradistinction to the opinion of Mayr and others, Malthus, according to Ospovat, had a great impact on Darwin. As one who had believed in harmony and perfect adaptation, Darwin received a shock when he read Malthus: 'When Darwin read Malthus ... the harmonious conception was shattered for him.' Ospovat does not wonder why Lamarck's struggle for existence did not have the same effect. The shock was clearly not sufficient to force Darwin to think again about catastrophes and mass extinctions. If Darwin really did get a shock it would seem it had little lasting effect. If Darwin was shocked by Malthus, why was he not shocked by Lamarck's observation that the planet was one vast slaughterhouse? Most research can find very little evidence that Malthus meant anything to Darwin.

151

In conclusion I get the impression from Ospovat's study that Darwin was just one of many naturalists engaged in biological studies especially to do with the species problem. Most naturalists specialise in one or few fields and had to fit their studies together with working for a living. Darwin was unique in not having to spend one hour on working for a living and so could devote every moment to collecting a massive amount about the subjects of the day and then adding natural selection to them.

In addition to his argument in favour of Darwin's 'impact factor', Mayr (1982) has suggested another reason why Darwinism is so important:

> The Darwinian revolution has been called the greatest of all scientific revolutions. It represented not merely the replacement of one scientific theory ('immutable species') by a new one, but it demanded a complete rethinking of man's concept of the world and of himself; more specifically, it demanded the rejection of some of the most widely held and most cherished beliefs of western man.

From this it appears that Mayr is unaware of the Seditious Acts that were introduced by the English government to try to stem the influence of the French Revolution and the flow of French science that followed. These Acts, as I have mentioned before, were intended to preserve those 'most cherished beliefs', principally to be found in the Hebrew Pentateuch. Does Mayr really imagine that other naturalists were not engaged on the species problem and man's involvement until after 1859? Darwin started his studies in 1837 but Patrick Matthew had published his Appendix in 1831. Edward Blyth wrote his seminal essays in 1835–7. In addition, Charles Lyell published Volume 2 of his *Principles of Geology* in 1832, in which he started the degrading of Lamarck's concepts. Even earlier, in an essay published in Edinburgh, Lamarck's philosophy was extolled – anonymously; that was in 1826 and the Seditious Acts were still in force. Furthermore, Robert Chambers and Herbert Spencer, a Lamarckian populariser, had been preaching evolution from about 1844. Mayr does not seem to have read some of the reviews of the *Origin of Species* when it first appeared. Several reviewers opened their statements with the comment that Darwin had revived and developed Lamarck's *Philosophy of Zoology* (Hull, 1973).

Mayr's statement appears a fair one but on closer examination it will be seen that it ignores completely what Darwin himself confessed in the sixth edition of the *Origin* (1872). In the introduction to a recent reprint of Lamarck's *Philosophy of Zoology,* André Pichot had this to say about Darwin's omission of man from all editions of the *Origin*:

> Ainsi, L'évêque d'Oxford lui reprocha de vouloir faire descendre l'homme du singe, alors que Darwin n'évoque nullement cette question dans son ouvrage. C'est Lamarck qui avait proposé une telle théorie, cinquante ans auparavant, dans sa *Philosophie Zoologique*, preuve que sa théorie n'était pas aussi oubliée qu'on veut bien le dire.

> ['The Bishop of Oxford reproached him for considering Man a descendant of a monkey, but Darwin made no mention of this subject in his work. It was Lamarck who had proposed such a theory, fifty years previously in *Philosophy of Zoology* and this was proof his theory had not been entirely forgotten.']

Pichot goes on to say that it was Lamarckian evolution followed by Darwinian evolution. Later on, with the introduction of genetics, neo-Darwinism was quietly adopted, followed by synthetic theory, and so allowed the complete elimination of Lamarck in English-speaking countries.

Evolutionary paradigms

From the beginning of the nineteenth century, fossils were fully recognised as the remains of animals and plants. For the most part these fossils resembled nothing that exists on earth today. Some very primitive plants and animals have survived from very early times and frequently show little structural change. The debate started in France about the relationship of past life-forms to present-day forms. Lamarck and Cuvier took opposite sides in the argument. Both got some things right and some wrong.

The first evolutionary paradigm is the Cuvier-Lamarck paradigm of 1808–32:

- Lamarck stressed descent from a common ancestor, the continuity of life-forms and the heredity link between life-forms. Present-day life-forms were descended from previous life-forms, including man – a completely naturalistic account of the history of the earth, involving gradual transmutation of species but with little attention paid to extinctions.
- Cuvier stressed catastrophes and mass extinctions of life-forms in the past history of the earth. He denied any heredity link between life-forms appearing after a catastrophe; species were miraculously created. He described animal forms in four main branches which introduced divergence. During the lifetime of species he postulated little structural change – the stability of species.

The second evolutionary paradigm is that of Patrick Matthew (1831), being a modified Cuvier-Lamarckian evolutionary paradigm. Matthew:

- accepted the catastrophes and mass extinctions of Cuvier;
- continued Cuvier's concept of divergence of species;
- agreed with Cuvier's stability of species;
- rejected Cuvier's miraculous creation of species;
- rejected Lamarck's transmutation of species and presents a completely naturalistic view of earth history;
- introduced the new concept of natural selection – a universal law of nature.

As in Lamarck's works, there is no hint of a Creator. Following a catastrophe, Matthew envisaged 'an unoccupied field would be formed for new diverging ramifications of life'.

The possibility of asteroids striking this planet had not been envisaged in Matthew's time. That asteroids have been responsible for catastrophes in the past is now being established (Clube and Napier 1982).

The third evolutionary paradigm dates from 1859; this is the Lyell-Darwin paradigm. Charles Lyell, in 1831, introduced a new concept of geology, which rejected the catastrophes and mass extinctions of Cuvier-Uniformitarianism. According to Lyell and most other naturalists, species were miraculously created, as Cuvier maintained. Darwin followed Lamarck's naturalistic view of the descent of species from a common ancestor. Darwin, however, in the *Origin of Species* introduced the Creator on several occasions but denied that his Creator had anything to do with the Hebrew Pentateuch. Darwin was also opposed to catastrophes and, indeed, declared they had been invented (Darwin, 1845). Darwin stressed the importance of natural selection.

Now that catastrophes and mass extinctions are recognised as real events in the history of the earth, the Lyell-Darwin paradigm has to be modified to take account of what they rejected. Indeed, because the Lyell-Darwin paradigm does not include the successive destructions that this planet has suffered from its inception, one may discount it in favour of Matthew's paradigm. There is Darwin's final view of the history of this planet:

> Thus, from the war of nature, from the famine and death, the most exalted object which we are capable of conceiving, namely, the production of the higher animals, directly follows. There is grandeur in this view of life, with its several powers, having been originally breathed by the Creator into a few forms or into one; and that, whilst this planet has gone cycling on according to the fixed law of gravity, from so simple a beginning endless forms beautiful and most wonderful have been, and are being evolved.

Here is Newton's equilibrium – a planet wondrous, ever spinning without a care in the universe. Clube (1995) has pointed out that:

> It is well known for example that very few of Newton's historical researches into Catastrophism and the role of comets and fireballs were published in his time with the result that astronomical science, and hence natural philosophy, tended thereafter to assume Uniformitarianism (i.e. non-catastrophic) characteristics.

Compare this with Matthew's view:

> The destructive liquid currents, before which the hardest mountains have been swept and comminuted into gravel, sand and mud, which intervened between and divided these epochs, probably extending over the whole surface of the globe, and destroying all living things, must have reduced existence so

155

much that an unoccupied field would be formed for new diverging ramifications of life.

In Matthew's time the causes of the successive mass destructions from extra-terrestrial sources were not established but the Lyell-Darwin paradigm did not even allow for their existence. As Clube (1995) has remarked, 'for long periods of time on earth, generations can follow generations under the impression that our cosmic environment is a continuous source of inspiration only to be succeeded for a while by generations aware of the fact that our cosmic environment can also be an intense source of foreboding'. Minor catastrophes have been recorded in recent times as in the past so, in this sense, Catastrophism is part of Uniformitarianism.

So how is one to rate Charles Darwin now?

His fame rests mainly on the *Origin of Species*. Had Sir Charles Lyell not forced the publisher, John Murray, to publish Darwin's manuscript as it was presented, the book would not have been published in the form it was – an Abstract without sources. The limited index remained unchanged right up to the sixth edition. The book was an instant success and was supported by influential scientists of the period. By avoiding the giving of sources the impression given to readers over the years was that all the concepts were original ideas of Darwin. Darwin realised that there was no proof that species had gradually changed. His devoted followers do not appear to understand this. Darwin wrote to George Bentham on 22 May 1863:

> The belief in natural selection must at present be grounded entirely on general considerations... When we descend to details, we can prove that not one species has changed (i.e. we cannot prove that a single species has changed), nor can we prove that the supposed changes are beneficial, which is the groundwork of the theory.

Lamarck had no proof either. He was criticised for this in his lifetime and it is the reason why he was dubbed a 'speculator' by French and English naturalists. Darwin, however, was hailed as a genius.

Charles Lyell introduced Lamarck's concepts in Volume 2 of his *Principles of Geology*. Here is part of what he wrote:

as the individuals of one of our species change their situation, climate, and manner of living, they change also, by little and little, the consistence and proportions of their parts, their form, their faculties, and even their organisation, in such a manner that everything in them comes at last to participate in the mutations to which they have been exposed ... in a word, at the end of many successive generations, these individuals, which originally belonged to another species, are transformed into a new and distinct species.

One cannot get more 'Darwinian' than that. But Lyell forgot all about this for 30 years when, for some reason, he reread Lamarck's books and then realised that there was no difference between Darwin's slow gradual change and Lamarck's slow gradual change. In 1875 Lyell revised the twelfth edition of *Principles of Geology*. In Chapter 34 he copied, word for word, what he had written in 1832. Few biologists appear to have noticed. The failure to find intermediate forms in the fossil record provided other evidence that there was no proof that species change.

It should be made clear that Lyell's 'surrounding conditions', which became Darwin's 'conditions of life', referred to Lamarck's comments in Chapter 7 of the *Philosophy of Zoology*. But Matthew's 'circumstance-suited' is nearer to Lamarck's speculation. It is obvious that Lamarck combined '*circonstances*' with 'habit', an aspect that was not appreciated by Weismann and other naturalists. Lyell followed Lamarck accurately with 'as to cause their habits, characters, and form to vary'. Darwin did not overlook 'habit' either:

On the whole, I think we may conclude that habit, use and disuse, have, in some cases, played a considerable part in the modification of the constitution, and of the structure of various organs, but that the effects of use and disuse have often been combined with, and sometimes overmastered by the natural selection of innate variations.

Darwin was just as much a speculator as Lamarck, as illustrated in the section in Chapter 4 of the *Origin* which employs Lamarck's term: 'Circumstances favourable for the production of new forms through natural selection'. It should be noted that 'circumstances favourable for new forms of life' occurs frequently in Lamarck's book.

In the *Historical Sketch* (1872), Darwin pointed out that both Lamarck and Matthew had stressed the importance of 'conditions of life'. Although Chapter 7 of *Philosophy of Zoology* is full of ingenious ideas, all are speculation and many naturalists considered them ridiculous. Lamarck's contemporaries and the contemporaries of Darwin recognised Lamarck as a speculator but revered him as a great botanist and the founder of invertebrate palaeontology. Darwin, too, in the *Historical Sketch*, tried to give a more accurate account of what Lamarck had achieved. It came too late, however, because the damage had been done many years before. The tragedy is that Darwinists appear to be unaware of what Darwin made clear in the *Historical Sketch* and so continue to ridicule Lamarck as Darwin did in his early years.

Although Lamarck speculated a great deal in an effort to bring natural law into the debate, he also produced extensive substantive data on botany and on zoology in two books. Lamarck is accredited with introducing and stimulating an interest in biology. Lamarck had no hard evidence that species changed by slow gradual stages, and it was because of this lack of evidence that Cuvier rejected his plausible and his more exaggerated speculations. Cuvier was in the same position though. Although he speculated about the 'miraculous creation' of species he was the greatest comparative anatomist in the world and was the founder of vertebrate palaeontology. In his day there was only limited evidence for his 'big five' catastrophes, mass extinctions and the apparent sudden appearance of new species in the fossil record. Lamarck was not opposed to local catastrophes but was sceptical about Cuvier's 'big five'. Both these naturalists paid the price for their rejection of each other's conclusions because they dropped out of evolutionary discussions in England.

A correspondent wrote Darwin to inform him that a Dr W.C. Wells had given a lecture before the Royal Society in 1813 that involved an exposition of natural selection. Darwin was very joyful at hearing that Patrick Matthew had been anticipated. Wells called his paper, 'An account of a White Woman, part of whose skin resembles that of the Negro'. In the *Historical Sketch* Darwin quoted from the paper 'by art, seems to be done with equal efficiency, though more slowly, in nature, in the formation of varieties of mankind, fitted for the country which they inhabit'. Darwin added, 'In this paper he distinctly recognises the principle of natural selection, and this is the first recognition which has been indicated: but he applies it only to man, and to certain characters alone'. It is odd that Darwin, who had spent so much time on Lamarck's works, should have missed this: 'Ce que nature fait avec beaucoup de temps, nous le faisons tous les jours, enchangeant nous-même subitement.' (*Philosophy of Zoology*, Chapter 7). ['What Nature takes so long to do, we can do quickly, with regard to a living plant, the circumstances in which it and all individuals of its species are to be found together.'] Lamarck then fills the chapter with numerous examples.

Lamarck goes on to state that all botanists are aware of this because the vegetables in their gardens demonstrate the power of the breeder in transforming the wild forms of vegetables into their domestic forms. What Lamarck had stated and Dr Wells had stated was no more than an old adage. But the breeder can only change the morphology of species. Nature, in some mysterious way, can actually produce *new* species. Darwin was probably thinking of Lamarck's statement when he wrote in the *Historical Sketch* that Lamarck 'seems to have been chiefly led to his conclusion on the gradual change of species by the analogy of domestic productions'. This was Darwin's starting point and, indeed, the basis on which he disagreed with Wallace's 1858 essay.

The simple manner in which Lamarck expressed the above statement gives one the impression that the relation of natural selection to artificial selection was well appreciated by French, if not all, naturalists of the period. After all, the eighteenth century was one of much improved breeding of farm animals. Lamarck was demonstrating, with all his speculations, the importance of introducing natural law into the new world of biology. Darwin made that abundantly clear. So, it is absurd for Darwinists to claim that Darwin was the first to dispense with 'the helping hand' when Darwin himself did not claim that, or that evolution through natural selection is Darwin's exclusive theory of evolution.

The eighteenth century was a period of intense breeding of farm animals and plants. Breeders were at last using selection as an important principle in achieving the product they wished to put on the market. This principle slipped over into the nineteenth century. Selection came to be present in all agricultural reports about breeding. Breeders would explain what particular characters they had selected. There were warnings that certain characters had to be selected in order to produce a certain new product. Selection and advertising developed together. However, in spite of all this intensive breeding in the early part of the nineteenth century, the publisher of the *Origin of Species*, a well-educated Scot, complained that he had never heard about selection in this new sense. Darwin protested, 'It is in all works on breeding.' He would know because he had spent a lot of time attending agricultural meetings.

Darwinism ended with the sixth edition of the *Origin of Species* in 1872, and its *Historical Sketch*. Pangenesis was not withdrawn because Darwin was very proud of it. He imagined he had found proof of Lamarck's inheritance of acquired characteristics. Lamarck did not have a theory of heredity. Darwin further supported Lamarck in dismissing Cuvier's catastrophes. Darwin's great contribution was to overcome the long silence and initiate debate, based on Lamarck's natural law, which continues today.

Steve Jones (1999) published what he calls an update of the *Origin of Species*, but Darwin's chapter on Recapitulation and Conclusion, together with the summary of several of the chapters, are included verbatim. Why? Jones makes much play about Darwin's suggestion that a bear could develop into a whale. This is an episode in Chapter 6, 'Difficulties with the theory':

> In North America the black bear was seen ... swimming for hours with widely opened mouth, thus catching, like a whale, insects in the water. Even in an extreme a case as this, if the supply of insects were constant, and if better competitors did not exist in the country, I can see no difficulty in a race of bears being rendered, by natural selection, more and more aquatic in their structure and habits, with larger and larger mouths, till a creature was produced as monstrous as a whale.

This is a Lamarckian view of one animal gradually changing into another animal. The update is confined to the first and second editions of the *Origin of Species*, so 'like a whale' (first edition) becomes 'almost like a whale' (second edition), but Jones does not mention that this speculation was dropped completely in later editions. Darwin was criticised, perhaps unfairly at the time, but was always anxious to satisfy his critics and the bear becoming a whale was not mentioned again.

In dealing with extinction, Jones makes this point: 'Because of the conservation movement, such catastrophes have become impossible to ignore.' This is an extraordinary comment to make because it was the discovery of the iridium layer at the K-T boundary that forced geologists and biologists to accept Cuvier's catastrophes. But there are still those who dispute that the catastrophes caused the mass extinctions and in this regard we are no further forward from Lamarck. Lamarck, Charles Lyell and Charles Darwin not only ignored extinctions, but considered they never happened. Jones mentions Cuvier on three occasions but never once makes it clear that it was he who discovered the major catastrophes and the four main branches of animal life, and further, that evolution was discontinuous. This custom of supporters of neo-Darwinism ignoring Cuvier is necessary for the maintenance of the Darwinian myth.

Although the *Origin* ran to six editions over a period of 12 years, little extra was added in spite of more discoveries of past catastrophes and mass extinctions. Mayr considers the 1859 edition to be the most important because of the impact it had. To enforce his belief, Harvard University published in 1964 a facsimile of the first edition with a foreword by Mayr. But did the first edition have such a great impact? Several authors, Secord (2000) among them, consider the impact was not as great as the impact that *The Vestiges of the Natural History of Creation* had on the middle-class in England. That book ran to ten editions from 1844 to 1855. This is when evolution was really discussed by the general public with Herbert Spencer the main populariser. Up until this time Darwin had not published a word.

Finally, let us once again review the evidence that the *Origin of Species* revived Lamarckism:

- The reviewers on the Continent, like Pictet, all regarded the *Origin* as revived Lamarckism.
- Because he considered the *Origin* to be revived Lamarckism, Whewell banned it from Trinity library. Whewell was a Catastrophist and the holder of the most prestigious academic post in England – the Mastership of Trinity College, Cambridge.
- In Chapter 5, 'Laws of variation', Darwin wrote: 'From the facts attached to the first chapter, I think there can be little doubt that use in our domestic animals strengthens and enlarges certain parts, and disuse diminishes them; and such

modifications are inherited'. So, Lamarck was not the only one who believed in the inheritance of acquired characters.

- Anyone who reads the *Origin* and then Lamarck's *Philosophy of Zoology* will realise how much Darwin took from that book.

- Wallace forced Darwin to alter the title of Chapter 4 of the *Origin*. 'Natural selection' was altered to 'Natural selection or the survival of the fittest' – a term introduced by the Lamarckian, Herbert Spencer.

- In 1863, Charles Lyell wrote Darwin to tell him that he now realised that there was no difference between Darwinism and Lamarckism.

- Lamarck's greatest mistake was to reject Cuvier's catastrophes and mass extinctions.

- The most important evidence that the *Origin* is Lamarckian is Darwin's own statement (see p. 100). Having described the Permian-Triassic extinction which swept away 90 per cent of animal life, Carl Zimmer wrote, 'The Permian-Triassic extinctions show that there is something to Cuvier's revolutions after all. Millions of species can be wiped away in a geological flash and the sort of life that takes over afterwards is often profoundly different from what came before.' No scientist prior to 1980 would have written those words because most biologists would have been ignorant of past catastrophes. It would seem that the only individual who realised that 'there is something to Cuvier's revolutions' was Patrick Matthew.

The suppression of Cuvier's catastrophes and mass extinctions is comparable to the suppression, by the Vatican, of the evidence that the earth and the planets orbited the sun. During the twentieth century, most distinguished biologists subscribed to the suppression of Cuvier's discoveries. In fact, his name was hardly mentioned. So are scientists as honest as they make themselves out to be?

162

5

Major Influences on Charles Darwin

A Recapitulation

If Darwin was concerned with promoting the concept of 'evolution by natural selection' he would have entered it on the first page of the *Origin of Species*. The reality is that Darwin's first and only reference to 'evolution' is to be found on three occasions on two pages at the very end of Chapter 7 of the sixth edition of 1872. No further reference to evolution is made in that edition, not even in the Recapitulation. It should be pointed out, however, that 'evolved' is the last word in all editions of the *Origin of Species*.

The first two chapters deal with variation under domestic and wild conditions. It was variation and its adaptability to varying conditions of life that Darwin was to pursue for the rest of his life. So, it seems that variation was the subject uppermost in Darwin's mind. Natural selection appears in the fourth chapter and was never associated with evolution. We know from Darwin's notebooks that between 1837 and 1844 he was reading extensively for evidence for the mutability of species. It is frequently claimed that Darwin had completed his theory by 1838. This is not what Darwin claimed. By 1844, in a letter to Hooker, he claimed that he was now 'almost convinced' of the mutability of species and in this he agreed with Lamarck. If Darwin was only 'almost convinced' in 1844, it is obvious that his theory was not established by 1838.

We know also from the bibliography assembled by Barrett *et al.* (1987) that Darwin had read the 1835–7 essays of Edward Blyth and had made contact with Blyth before he set sail for India in 1842. These essays are discussed in Notebook C.

We should find evidence of those influences on Darwin in the first pages of the *Origin of Species*. The very first sentence is:

> When we look to the individuals of the same variety or sub-variety of our older cultivated plants and animals, one of the first points which strikes us is that they generally differ from each other more than do the individuals of any one species or variety in a state of nature.

If we turn to Blyth's essays we find a classification of varieties and then this: 'These simple variations occur both in wild and in domesticated animals, but are much more frequent in the latter, and are commonly observed in all breeds and true varieties'. It was very discerning of Darwin to realise the worth of Blyth's essays. It was variation and Blyth's essays that Darwin concentrated on in the 1868 publication, *Variation in Animals and Plants under Domestication*; and that was the subject of the first chapter in the *Origin*. In the introduction to this book there is this statement: 'Mr Blyth has freely communicated to me his stores of knowledge on this [i.e. variation] and all other related subjects.' Would Darwin have introduced Blyth in this fashion if Blyth had not had a strong influence on him?

There are over 40 references to the published work of Blyth in the 1868 book, but most of them in the *Origin of Species* are not referenced to Blyth. Darwin refused to give his sources for the *Origin of Species*; he made that clear in the introduction that is the same, word for word, in all editions.

Returning now to the first page of the *Origin*, we find this statement: 'It seems pretty clear that organic beings must be exposed during several generations to the new conditions of life to cause any appreciable amount of variation, and that when the organisation has once began to vary, it generally continues to vary for many generations'. This is Lamarckism.

So what Darwin was concerned to proclaim first was the universality of variation and its controlling influence, the conditions of life. In doing so the reviewers of the 1859 edition of the *Origin* all claimed Darwin had revived Lamarckism (Hull 1973). The *Origin of Species* is not about evolution, it is about variation and its adaptability to changing conditions of life.

The first introduction of species 'evolving' came in an essay of

1826 in the *Edinburgh New Philosophical Journal*, attributed to Robert Grant. Grant was a dedicated Lamarckian, but Lamarck never employed the word 'evolved'. He was concerned with change and at the same time continuity of life over immense time. Cuvier had shown in his excavations in the Paris Basin that a succession of animals and plants had occurred in the past history of the earth, but denied evolution of the animals and plants that were so different in each succession and which in the fossil record appeared suddenly.

Lamarck's grave mistake was to reject Cuvier's major catastrophes and mass extinctions. Charles Lyell followed Lamarck in his *Principles of Geology*. Darwin and generations of biologists and geologists believed Cuvier's catastrophes and mass extinctions never happened. Darwin knew that the ammonites had suddenly disappeared at the end of the Cretaceous. He was also aware of the very sudden appearance of the Angiosperms. Furthermore, he was aware that there was no proof that a species in its lifetime could change into another species; he made this admission in a letter to George Bentham in 1863. That a species could change into another species in its lifetime was the implication in Lamarck's view of the history of life. If evolution means an unfolding process, which would be

Edward Blyth

165

Lamarck's view, it would be contrary to the fact that species do *not* change in their lifetime. Mayr (1982) has suggested that this is the reason why Darwin avoided using the word 'evolution'.

In 1871 and again in 1874 Darwin published *The Descent of Man.* Darwin was obsessed with sexual selection and it was to this subject that he returned with Part 2. This part, headed 'Sexual selection', is the larger part of the book. How did Darwin come to be interested in sexual selection? In the *Origin*, John Hunter is accredited with having introduced the term 'secondary sexual characters'. It is obvious that this term was still in Darwin's mind because Part 2 begins:

> With animals which have their sexes separated, the males necessarily differ from the females in their organs of reproduction, and these afford the primary sexual characters. But the sexes differ in what Hunter has called secondary sexual characters, which are not directly connected with the act of reproduction.

It is to Hunter's concept of secondary sexual characters that most of Part 2 is devoted. Darwin gives the Hunterian source, *Essays and Observations* (1861) and expresses his admiration for the 'illustrious Hunter'. There is evidence that Darwin read these essays during the period 1837 to 1844 (Barrett *et al.* 1987). It is probable that Richard Owen directed Darwin's attention to these yet unpublished essays on some occasion when he was identifying Darwin's fossils.

In the 1874 edition of *The Descent of Man* Darwin admits that there is nothing original in his book because Lamarck had 'long ago' concluded that man had a simian origin. In Lamarck's *Philosophy of Zoology* there is a list of the races of man. Darwin also has a chapter on the races of man in which several authors are cited as postulating different numbers of the races of man. Lamarck is ignored but Buffon is accredited with six races and that is the number that Lamarck has in *Philosophy of Zoology.*

Lamarck classified man as a mammifer with an opposable thumb. When Charles Lyell discovered this he was horrified. In Part 1 of Lamarck's *Philosophy of Zoology*, a list of various orders of animal life is discussed. Man is presented as a mammifer of six varieties with an opposable thumb. This anatomical structure differentiates man from the orang-utan.

In Part 2 of his book, Darwin returned to his main interest in variations in animals and plants. There is very little about natural selection in *The Descent of Man*. It is obvious that Darwin chose 'descent' rather than 'evolution', which is closer to Lamarck's view of the history of the evolution of man.

Darwinists do not seem to have noticed that Darwin admitted in the 1874 edition that there is nothing original in his book. What was original was the observations of Hunter, the importance of which Darwin had the prescience to grasp. This was the stimulus that set Darwin the task of collecting a vast amount of evidence from published reports. Although Hunter's observations are frequently given, there are several other of his observations that have been omitted. Hunter, Darwin pointed out, had observed that colour could influence sexual selection. It is odd, therefore, that Darwin did not mention that Hunter and St Hilaire had both reported that elderly hen pheasants could assume the spectacular plumage of the cock pheasant. Darwin commented on this phenomenon in a notebook. He would not have been able to explain this change, but other examples of reversion he would attempt to explain with his theory of Pangenesis. When the female hormones fade androgens that play no important function during the fertile period come to dominate the physiology of the female of the species.

In the *Origin of Species* Darwin mentions Hunter only once. In *The Descent of Man* Darwin is more generous and makes it clear from the very beginning of Part 2 that Hunter's observations were the basis from which he started his searches in the literature.

In his 1872 *Historical Sketch* Darwin had already stated that Lamarck had demonstrated that man had descended from previous species. The fact that Lamarck classified man as just another class of mammal was shocking to Regency and Victorian English naturalists and was the cause of his being banned in England, until revived and developed by Darwin. Unfortunately, Darwin is remembered more for his ridiculing of Lamarck than for his later admission.

Although Darwin altered little about his sources in later editions of the *Origin of Species*, in his other books he did reveal his main sources: Lamarck, Edward Blyth and John Hunter.

In 1981, Princeton University Press reprinted the 1871 edition of *The Descent of Man* with an introduction by John T. Bonner and Robert M. May. Here, these authors explain why the 1871 edition rather than the 1874 edition was reprinted: 'The reason is partly that Darwin had an unfortunate habit, in his revisions, of rewriting some of the freshness out of the initial work.' The other reason or reasons for selecting the 1871 edition are not alluded to. Harvard authors took the same attitude to the *Origin of Species* when the 1859 edition was reprinted.

Although Darwin, in his introduction to the 1871 edition, casually confesses that there is nothing original in the book, he goes much further in the 1874 edition. The reason now that there is nothing original is because Lamarck concluded 'long ago' that man was of simian origin.

One has only to read the introduction to the 1874 edition to realise that Darwin's contemporary critics had forced him to confess several other important facts. Having reprinted the 1871 edition in 1981, another generation of biologists are kept in the dark about the sources of *The Descent of Man*.

Bonner and May continue:

The reason for reassessing Charles Darwin's *The Descent of Man* in 1981, one hundred and ten years after its first appearance, is that it addresses an extraordinary number of problems that are, at the moment, on the minds of many biologists, psychologists, anthropologists, and philosophers.

Had Bonner and May read the book more carefully they would have realised that the same problems were actively addressed by eighteenth-century medical practitioners.

What is not in the introduction is any reference to Hunter. The second sentence of Part 2 has already been referred to, so who is this Hunter whose concept of 'secondary sexual characters' forms the heading of every chapter? Bonner and May do not appear to have noticed.

Perhaps Darwin assumed that everyone would know who Hunter was. He knew exactly who Hunter was because it was in the John Hunter Museum that Richard Owen had identified all those fossils that Darwin had sent back from the *Beagle*. Hunter (1728–93) was regarded by the end of the eighteenth century as the initiator of scientific surgery and it was in his honour that the Royal College of Surgeons of England was founded. Richard Owen revered Hunter and regarded him as the greatest natural philosopher since Aristotle.

So, once again Darwin did what he was good at – picking up

168

good ideas from other people and searching endlessly for more and more evidence.

Although 'Sexual selection' is the heading to Part 2 of *The Descent of Man*, the heading of every chapter is 'secondary sexual characters'. This indicates that sexual selection is derived from and implied in Hunter's concept of secondary sexual characters. Darwin even refers to Hunter's observation of a zebra on heat refusing a male ass until the ass had been painted with stripes. This was an example Hunter had used to demonstrate that colour could influence sexual selection. Darwin went on to gather more evidence for Hunter's observations. It is really amazing how Darwinists develop a blind spot when they encounter anything that might interfere with the myth they have ruthlessly developed over the generations.

Evidence has been presented in this chapter and all the others in this book that the three major influences on Darwin were the writings of Lamarck, Edward Blyth and John Hunter. Darwin denied ever having read Matthew's book and its Appendix, so we must take his word for it because nowhere in the written notes is the name of Matthew to be found. Mayr and others have shown that many of Darwin's statements are very similar to those of Matthew. It seems to be another case of an originator being ignored and later on someone else popularising the theory and coming to be accepted as the originator. Even when Matthew announced in April 1860 that evolution by natural selection was discussed in the Appendix of his book, no one took any notice except Darwin, who acknowledged Matthew's priority in letters and in the *Historical Sketch.*

What was not a major influence on Darwin were the Galapagos finches that were not even mentioned in the *Origin of Species*. After an exhaustive survey of the numerous reports about Darwin and the Galapagos finches that had become a legend, Sulloway (1982) came to the conclusion that the evidence refuted that the legend was crucial to Darwin's evolutionary theory. Sulloway declared that 'In spite of the legend's manifest contradictions with historical fact, it successively holds sway today in the major textbooks of biology and ornithology ... it has become, in fact, one of the most widely circulated legends in the history of the life sciences, ranking with the famous stories of Newton and the apple and of Gallileo's experiments at the Leaning Tower of Pisa, as a classic textbook account of the origins of modern science.' Darwin had received at Montevideo in 1832 the second volume of Lyell's *Principles of*

Geology that contained a full exposition of Lamarck's evolutionary theory. By the time the *Beagle* left the Galapagos in 1835, Darwin had read over and over again that exposition. His first subject of research on returning to England in 1836 was to collect, between 1837 and 1844, more evidence for Lamarck's transmutation of species and he adhered to that theory to the end of his days.

6

The Consequences of Punctuated Equilibria

For over 20 years two American naturalists have tried to convince their scientific colleagues that Uniformitarianism and the slow graduated change of species require major modification. This involves Sir Charles Lyell who introduced the new geology of Uniformitarianism devoid of catastrophes and mass extinction of plants and animals, and Charles Darwin who carried on the Lamarckian idea that species mutated by slow graduated changes. The two naturalists are Stephen Jay Gould and Niles Eldredge (Eldredge and Gould 1972) who find themselves caught up in an argument with other devoted Darwinists about the validity of Darwin's gradual change and the speed at which species appear and disappear in the fossil record. Much heated argument has been generated by the two naturalists in claiming that there have been periods of rapid speciation and that during the lifetime of species there is little or no structural change. The fossil record indicates that there is structural stasis during the lifetime of species. The orthodox Darwinists maintain that even these periods of rapid speciation can be embraced by neo-Darwinism. What neither side in this argument seem to be aware of is that Gould and Eldredge have resurrected old facts and opinions which now reflect accurately the past history of the world. None of the protagonists, in this argument, appear to have read the sixth edition of the *Origin of Species* and its incorporated *Historical Sketch*. Nor do the protagonists appear to be aware that Charles Lyell wrote to Darwin in 1863 to say he had done an injustice to Lamarck in 1832, and that he could now see no difference between Lamarckism and Darwinism. It is not made clear, in their statements, that catastrophes and mass extinctions, as described by Cuvier, are now recognised as realities in the history of the world.

Thomas Huxley tried to convince Darwin that there could be periods of rapid speciation but Darwin would have none of it. Here are Darwin's statements, which he stubbornly adhered to:

> If we look to long enough intervals of time, geology plainly declares that species have all changed, and they have changed in the manner required by the theory, for they have changed slowly and in a gradual manner.
>
> Why should not Nature take a sudden leap, from structure to structure? On the theory of natural selection we can clearly understand why She should not, for natural selection acts only by taking advantage of slight successive variations, She can never take a great leap, but must advance by short and sure, although slow steps.

Darwin did not seem to appreciate that these dogmatic statements did not support his own evidence as recorded in the chapter 'On the imperfection of the geological record'.

Niles Eldredge (1986) counters Darwin's statements with 'Indeed, most gradual changes with which I am familiar in the fossil record seem to be more to-ing and fro-ing – a sort of oscillation within a spectrum of possible states'. So Gould and Eldredge argue that, during the lifetime of species, there is little structural change and species maintain their stability. Darwin would counter this with: 'The Silurian Lingula differs little from the living species of this genus; whereas most of the other Silurian Molluscs and all of the Crustaceans have changed greatly'. It would appear there is some disagreement as to what constitutes 'change'.

Darwin spent seven years classifying cerripedes so he was able to form some conclusions about the graduated change of species over time. Although Cuvier was adamant that vertebrate species remain stable during their lifetime, he did concede that superficial changes, like colour of hair or skin, could occur, but there was no change in the main organs – the skeleton, the brain, the lungs, the heart and circulation. Eldredge's 'too-ing and fro-ing' is not a scientific statement and Darwin's 'changed greatly' is no clearer. Darwin pointed out in the *Historical Sketch* (1872) that Lamarck had reached his conclusion about species evolution 'by the almost perfect gradation of forms in certain groups'. There is evidence that other species have appeared suddenly in the fossil record and as suddenly have disappeared.

How natural selection achieves stasis or triggers change remains a mystery although conditions of life, in some way, seem to be involved. Eldredge (1986) points out that in 1859, 'Every naturalist was aware of the stability of species including Darwin who ignored this fact because he was bent on ignoring Cuvier.' 'But stasis was conveniently dropped', writes Eldredge,

> as a feature of life's history to be reckoned with in evolutionary biology. And stasis has continued to be ignored until Gould and I showed that stability is a real aspect of life's history which must be confronted ... it posed no fundamental threat to the basic notion of evolution itself ... Darwin felt that he had to undermine the older (and ultimately biblically based) doctrine of species fixity.

But the biblical doctrine was opposed to transmutation of species as a concept in itself. Cuvier was certainly opposed to it for rather dubious religious reasons. But Cuvier recognised that in the fossil record as well as in extant species there was stability during the lifetime. With that background he was bitterly opposed to Lamarck who was the first to postulate the mutation of species and the continuity of life-forms. Considering circumstances favourable to natural selection, Darwin commented: 'Though Nature grants vast periods of time for the work of natural selection, She does not grant an indefinite period; for as all organic beings are striving, it may be said, to seize on each place in the economy of nature, if any one species does not become modified and improved in a corresponding degree with its competitors, it will soon be exterminated.' To this Eldredge (1986) answers, 'stasis is the norm'.

Early reviewers of the *Origin of Species* were of the same opinion but were also aware that Darwin had taken the slow, gradual transmutation from Lamarck. Francois Pictet (1809–72) had this to say:

> This learned writer, in reviving the celebrated theory of Lamarck but in a more judicious and acceptable form, thinks like him that the diverse zoological characters are the product of gradual

modifications. There are, it is true, profound differences between his theory and that of Lamarck.

Pictet was also convinced that 'stasis was the norm':

> Everything in living nature seems to proclaim this tendency of the conservation of specific forms. When for thousands of years, we see acorns constantly producing oak trees, which are alike in their carriage and appearance down to the accidental details, when we reflect on the powerful and mysterious force which acts on this little grain in order to bring about so constant a development, when we see the same phenomenon repeated in all organisms, would not the force of induction that permanence of form is the rule and variation is only an exception.
>
> (Hull 1973)

With such confident support from the contemporaries of Darwin, one wonders why Eldredge wishes to reinvent Darwin, especially when he rejects his fundamental theory of gradual change: 'We pointed out that palaeontologists clung to the myth of gradual adaptive transformation even in the face of plain evidence to the contrary' (Eldredge 1995). Eldredge finds himself so opposed to Darwinian principles that he now wishes to reinvent Darwin. One may note in this book the slanging match that has been going on between the opposing sides in the argument about the stability of species in their lifetime and the periods of rapid speciation. Both sides seem to be unaware of the history of the species argument prior to the publication of the *Origin of Species*. Darwin did not introduce a historical background to the *Origin of Species* but expected readers to engage immediately in a discussion on varieties. Eldredge and Gould must know very well the history of biology from the nineteenth century (as described in the preceding chapters) but have not betrayed this in their writings. It is perhaps too embarrassing for Darwinists to contemplate. The conclusion that Gould and Eldredge have now reached is that Lyell, and then Darwin, got the history of the world all wrong because they ignored the possibility of catastrophes and mass extinctions.

Eldredge (1995), a devoted Darwinist, considered that he and Gould were introducing a new concept: 'We proposed a sort of pruning process, in which only some of the many species extant at

174

any one time would persist and give rise to descendants.' Darwin's perception of extinction was usually similar to Lyell's as in this example: 'by unperceived injurious agencies, and that these same unperceived agencies are amply sufficient to cause rarity and finally extinction'. However, in the Conclusion to the *Origin of Species* is a statement which anticipates Eldredge's supposed new idea: 'for the manner in which all organic beings are grouped shows that the greater number of species of each genus, and all the species of many genera, have left no descendants but have become utterly extinct'. Patrick Matthew (1831) recognised that some species would not reproduce descendants: 'those who possess not the requisite strength ... fall prematurely without reproduction'. This surely indicates the concept had been recognised by naturalists earlier on in the nineteenth century. Matthew, in reviewing Darwin's *The Descent of Man* (1871) made the observation, missed by Darwin, that like any other species there must be several varieties out of which *Homo sapiens* would eventually emerge and the rest would become extinct. Only in recent times has this concept been recognised as more fossils of parts of early man have been found. If only Lyell and Darwin had not persisted with their incredible rejection of catastrophes and mass extinctions, the history of the world would not have followed the distorted path it did. Only in recent times has 'the restless earth' been recognised. How the theory proposed by Eldredge and Gould can account for the absence of fossils of intermediate forms in the geological record in not clear.

Eldredge (1995) devotes a sentence in passing to Cuvier's catastrophes and admits that: 'Once again we confront patterns in life's history well known to nineteenth-century naturalists but [which] have been generally ignored under the Darwinian evolutionary paradigm.' But there is no mention of the fact that it was Charles Lyell who refuted catastrophes and mass extinctions by introducing Uniformitarianism. What Gould and Eldredge have failed to make clear is that the history of the world was bound to be wrongly portrayed from the moment that Lyell introduced the new geology. Darwin compounded the problem by claiming that catastrophes had been 'invented'.

Eldredge appears to be unaware of what Darwin had written about Lamarck in the *Historical Sketch* of 1872. Dealing with Lamarck is the by now familiar statement, 'In these works he upholds that all species, including man, are descended from other

175

species...' and so on. If Darwin was aware that in Lamarck's *Philosophy of Zoology* man was assessed as just another class of mammal, why is Eldredge not aware of it? Another fact that Eldredge appears not to be aware of is the early introduction of natural selection by Patrick Matthew (1831) which even Darwin acknowledged in the 1872 *Historical Sketch*, but Eldredge (1995) states that, 'Natural selection is Darwin's term, counterpoised with "artificial selection".'

Eldredge (1995) is mistaken when he claims that 'Design, according to pre-Darwinian, religiously-imbued tradition, implies a Designer.' The biochemist Behe (1996) is of the opinion that a designer is at work and even Darwin himself involved the Creator on numerous occasions in the *Origin*. When it came to discussing organs of extreme perfection, Darwin had this to say: 'and may we not believe that a living optical instrument might thus be formed as superior to one of glass, as the works of the Creator are to those of Man' (*Origin*, Ch. 6).

Lyell and then Darwin were profoundly wrong in supposing that the history of the earth was just one slow continuous process of change. It is now obvious to discerning naturalists, as it was to Cuvier and Matthew, that the history of the earth has involved periods of intense upheaval and periods of relative quiescence. By refuting catastrophes and mass extinctions Lyell and Darwin were unable to link change to historical events – to catastrophes. Faced with apparently sudden appearances of new life forms in the fossil record, Darwin had no option but to blame the imperfection of the fossil record and to argue against sudden change as he did in the following passage: 'The abrupt manner in which whole groups of species suddenly appear in certain formations, has been urged by several palaeontologists.' Darwin countered with: 'that natural selection will always act with extreme slowness, I fully admit ... New species have appeared very slowly, one after the other, both on the land and in the waters.' Other contemporaries produced different facts. Richard Owen, a bitter opponent of Darwin, followed Cuvier in stressing the lack of structural change during the lifetime of species: 'The last Ichthyosaurs, by which the genus disappears in the chalk, is hardly distinguishable specifically from the first Ichthyosaurs which abruptly introduce that strange form of sea-lizard. The oldest Pterodactyl is as thorough and complete a one as the latest.' Louis Agassiz, another opponent of Darwin, was

Cuvier's supporter as well: 'Between two successive geological periods changes have taken place among plants and animals. But none of those primordial forms of life which naturalists call species are known to have changed during any of these periods.' The coelacanth, still living deep in the Indian Ocean, has not changed in 200 million years. The Brachiopod Lingula has survived 400 million years with little morphological change. Eldredge would attribute the longevity to a low level of specialisation; to being generalist rather than specialist. But the golden mole, able to live in five habitats, has survived for 25 million years (Gorman and Stone 1990).

Gould (2002) may rightly complain that there was 'an unconscious conspiracy of silence' and 'non-reporting of punctuated equilibrium', but then engaged in a conspiracy of silence and non-reporting of Patrick Matthew's grasp of the same concept. Gould and Eldredge were forced to withdraw rash speculations about punctuated equilibria. Matthew was not a speculator but considered that an important event, such as a major catastrophe, would provide 'an open field for new diverging ramifications of life'. This, in fact, was what happened. Any further comment would be sheer speculation. The pity is that Matthew was marginalised by the first Darwinists because of the bias, at that time, against catastrophes. Now, as a latter-day Darwinist, Gould (2002), voicing the importance of catastrophes, has relegated Matthew to a brief footnote.

Darwin, in the *Origin*, never linked Cuvier's name with catastrophes. Eldredge and Gould (1972) tend to play down catastrophes and mass extinctions and concentrate on periods of rapid speciation and species stasis during the periods of quiescence. They are devoted Darwinists and find themselves in an embarrassing position. Periods of rapid speciation and species stasis are anathema to orthodox Darwinism. That is the problem. Accept these concepts of catastrophes and mass extinctions resurrected by Gould and Eldredge and the main tenets of Darwinism are refuted.

Gould and Eldredge's punctuated equilibria might give the impression that they undermine Uniformitarianism and neo-Darwinism, and so it was obvious that a crisis would develop. Most biologists, it would appear, are standing on the sidelines. Even by covering their tracks, by avoiding extensive reference to Cuvier or Lamarck, few converts to punctuated equilibria have appeared. Eldredge (1986) employs the term 'stability of species' to indicate the lack of structural change during the lifetime of species. Cuvier also used this exact term (Coleman 1964). Edward Blyth, who translated Cuvier's *Le Règne Animal*, used the same term although, like Cuvier, he was dead against transmutation of species for religious reasons. But, in the lifetime of extant species, Blyth saw every attempt by the species to maintain their stability; the localising principle was the term he employed to designate the stability of species.

Now that phyletic gradualism is regarded as old-fashioned, Matthew becomes an important figure in the new view of evolution. Eldredge (1986) employs the term 'steady state'. Matthew used the same term to indicate the stability of species in their epoch. More frequently, as we have seen, Matthew used the term 'circumstance-suited' to portray the stability of species in their lifetime, and this indicates that Matthew was aware of Lamarck's *'circonstance'*. From this perspective it would appear that Matthew was a far more discerning naturalist than Darwin.

Huxley failed to change Darwin's mind about the possibility of periods of rapid speciation, and yet there are Darwinists today who deny that the evidence of Gould, Eldredge and others lies outside neo-Darwinism. It is now well recognised that the turnover of mammals is much more rapid than of bivalves. The conditions of life, as Lamarck observed, could explain the rapid speciation and extinction of mammals caused by more competition for resources.

The modern view is that changes can be rapid: 'Darwin thought that evolution occurred by imperceptible small steps. Today we know that some of the steps have been abrupt' (Haldane 1959). Admittedly, more is known about the rapid speciation of mammals today than in the mid-nineteenth century. Although Matthew's statements appear to be close to what Gould and Eldredge are now arguing, it would be difficult for them to recognise, at this late stage, what Matthew stood for. They are 'reinventing' Darwin, even though he rejected Cuvier's catastrophes and would have nothing to do with the abrupt appearance and disappearance of species in the fossil record. It is perhaps unsettling for Darwinists to consider that Gould and Eldredge have, unwittingly, returned the history of the organic and inorganic world to the basic state it was in by 1831.

Punctuated equilibrium does provide a more accurate view of earth history and renders old-fashioned the Lyell-Darwin evolutionary paradigm (see Chapter 4). Patrick Matthew's modified Cuvier-Lamarckian evolutionary paradigm, with catastrophes and mass extinctions followed by apparently new species taken into account, provides a more accurate view of what happened during the history of the earth after animal and plant life first appeared.

Clube (1995) has stressed the point that:

It is well known for example that very few of Newton's historical researches into Catastrophism and the role of comets and fireballs were published in his lifetime with the result that astronomical science, and hence natural philosophy, tended thereafter to assume Uniformitarianism (i.e. non-catastrophe) characteristics... The point to be noted then is that there are positive and negative, both light and dark, sides to the inspiration provided by astronomical phenomena in the past, and we seriously misunderstand human history if we suppose our celestial environment never impinges adversely upon the earth. Quite simply, the enlightened or supposedly Uniformitarian view of nature these last two hundred years has diverted attention from adverse celestial inputs and there is now a serious risk, especially from within the fastness of an ivory tower, that inspiration's commonest inducement, the appeal to a sublime principle, will continue to press our cosmic perspective and our cultural endeavour towards some kind of paradisical extreme.

Few physicists are so aware as Clube of the potential celestial-induced catastrophes and mass extinctions which may in future involve this planet as they have done in the past. Few biologists are aware of Clube's realism and foreboding because, as has been explained, Charles Lyell followed by Darwin argued for a Uniformitarian history of the earth but at the same time refuted with catastrophes and mass extinctions. This Uniformitarian view has been the received wisdom for geologists and biologists for the last two hundred years, but punctuated equilibria fit into Uniformitarianism.

Lord Kelvin (1868) attacked Lyell's Uniformitarianism: 'There cannot be uniformity. The earth is filled with evidences that it has not been going on forever in the same state, and that there is progress of events towards a state infinitely different from the present.' But Kelvin was not aware of the repeated catastrophes in the past history of the earth, nor that they were every bit a part of Uniformitarianism as the ice ages.

The discovery of a layer of iridium at the K-T boundary by Alvarez *et al.* (1980) caused embarrassment among palaeontologists. Alvarez concluded that a meteorite had struck the earth and caused the extinction of the dinosaurs in a catastrophe 65 million years ago. A furious argument ensued. Scientists had been brought up on Lamarckian-Darwinian gradualism devoid of catastrophes and mass extinctions. Gould and Eldredge considered that their punctuation theory had been confirmed. It was, in fact, confirmation of Cuvier's discoveries, described in 1808. Along with the dinosaurs, the ammonites were made extinct. Darwin knew that the ammonite had suddenly disappeared at the end of the Cretaceous but still persisted in rejecting Cuvier. Fundamental Darwinists rejected the conclusion that the extinction of the dinosaurs was due to a catastrophe. There were those who argued that there was evidence that animals were gradually becoming extinct prior to the catastrophe. Subsequently, the region struck by the meteorite was discovered in the Gulf of Mexico, adjacent to the Yucatan Peninsula. Most scientists are now prepared to accept the catastrophic explanation for the extinction, but the debate continues.

Cosmology is the concern of physicists, but there are physicists not satisfied with their own disciplines who are searching for 'a theory of everything', turning to other disciplines in the hope of finding coordinating clues to a unity of knowledge and a logical system. Lee Smolin (1997) is such a physicist, and has attempted to link cosmology to Darwin's natural selection. Smolin is unaware, apparently, that Darwin would have nothing to do with celestial debris or anything else causing catastrophes and mass extinctions on this planet. Smolin concluded that the most impressive aspect of natural selection was the creation of the universe itself. Unwittingly perhaps, he has extended Matthew's argument that natural selection is a universal law of nature, to explain how the evolution of the universe came about. How the right ingredients, as it were – carbon, oxygen and so on – combined to make life.

Concepts involving notions derived from combined disciplines are frequently confused and misleading because within each discipline there are serious disagreements which have not aroused wide publicity beyond the disciplines themselves. If Lee Smolin were to renounce his 'cosmological selection' perhaps he would end up with our universe as the 'fittest'.

The physicists Bak and Snepen (1994) are not convinced that mass extinctions are necessarily caused by catastrophes. Using a computer model based on species fitness, they claim to mimic what happens in the real world. 'Fitness' is not really a scientific term. Was Tyrannosaurus Rex less 'fit' than a small contemporary mammal? This is not to deny that the last generation of dinosaurs would have become extinct as the previous generations had done. The reality of the catastrophe at the end of the Cretaceous has many facts in its favour – the iridium layer discovered by Alvarez *et al.*, the impact area in the Gulf of Mexico, that life was mainly affected in the northern hemisphere and that all life-forms over five kilos were wiped out. There was also damage to small life-forms but because they were more numerous many survived.

The fossil record of the evolution of mammals – like reptiles in remote times indicates that some reptiles, such as Thrinaxodon or Oligokyphus or Lystrosaurus, were the remote ancestors of the mammals. However, the lack of intermediate forms in the fossil record is quite a mystery. What is further disturbing is the absence of intermediate forms at the molecular level as well. No intermediate form of cytochrome has so far been found between bacterial and eukaryotic cytochrome. The amount of DNA in the genome does not increase steadily up the supposed evolutionary scale. This leaves the source of new genes as another mystery unless they can emerge from the 'nonsense' DNA which is the large part of DNA for which no function has yet been found.

Many biologists would agree with the following statement: 'The known fossil record fails to document a single example of phyletic [gradual] evolution accomplishing a major morphological transition and hence [there is] no evidence that the gradualistic model can be valid' (Stanley 1979). The nearest thing to gradual evolution is to be found in the evolution of mammalian characteristics among groups of reptiles in very remote times.

To the sixth edition of the *Origin of Species* Darwin added a new chapter (Chapter 7) which discussed miscellaneous objections to his theory. His argument was directed mainly at the ideas of one Mr Mivart who had been arguing for the abrupt appearance of species. This was Cuvier's concept based on the apparent absence of intermediate forms in the fossil record. Although the last word in most editions of the *Origin of Species* is 'evolved', Darwin appears to have avoided the use of this word again until the new chapter in the sixth edition. By 1872, evolution rather than natural selection was being discussed. Whatever the reason for Darwin's sudden conversion to evolution, he expressed his enthusiasm on three occasions on two pages:

> Everyone who believes in slow and gradual evolution, will admit that specific changes may have been as abrupt and as great as any single variation which we meet with under nature, or even under domestication. But as species are more variable when domesticated or cultivated than under their natural conditions, it is not probable that such great and abrupt variations have often occurred under nature.
>
> (p.201)

> That many species have been evolved in an extremely gradual manner, there can hardly be a doubt.
>
> (p.202)

And then: 'Many large groups of facts are intelligible only on the principle that species have been evolved by very small steps' (p.202). These statements all reflect Lamarck's influence on Darwin.

Darwin ends the chapter by addressing the issues raised with Mivart:

> He who believes that some ancient form was transformed suddenly through an internal force or tendency into, for instance, one furnished with wings, will be almost compelled, in opposition to all analogy, that many individuals varied simultaneously... To believe all this is so, as it seems to me, to enter into the realms of miracle, and to leave those of Science.
>
> (p.204)

Darwinists, with this dismissal of abrupt change, can hardly claim today that punctuated equilibrium can be embraced within Darwinism. In any case, Buffon countered earlier catastrophic interpretations of nature (in *Theory of the Earth*, 1749 and *Epochs of Nature*, 1778). Thomas Burnet's *Sacred History of the Earth* (1680–91) is an example of someone able to look at areas of wasteland and great

182

mountains with wonder and pleasure while still regarding them as evidence of past disasters: 'And yet those mountains we are speaking of, to confess the truth, are nothing but great ruins'. During the next century the Enlightenment was causing all sections of society to study nature but the debate concerning the causation of mountains and landscapes continued. The Vulcanists and Neptunists argued fiercely, the early Romantic movement stressed the beauty of nature, but by the end of the eighteenth century there were those, like Ramon de Carbonnières, who still resisted past disasters: 'Great commotions, irregular accidents, disastrous events have not scattered, drawn, or mutilated their debris. Time alone has acted with its powerful but light hand' (Rosen 1996).

Three centuries have passed between Newton's refusal to countenance any disturbance of the equilibrium he had established, and the punctuated equilibrium of Gould and Eldredge. Nearly two centuries have passed since Patrick Matthew corrected the mistakes of Lamarck and Cuvier and stressed the importance of universal catastrophes, which have only recently been addressed. As we have seen, Lyell's Uniformitarianism includes catastrophes, but Lyell and Darwin's rejection of catastrophes has misled generations of scientists. It is now time to reassess their theories and a recent publication has done precisely that (Dempster 1966).

It is also high time that Darwinists, all of them, acknowledge the importance of Cuvier's discoveries in any consideration of evolution.

7

Lamarck, Decandolle and Natural Selection

It is generally believed that Charles Darwin introduced evolution through natural selection. It is true that his famous book the *Origin of Species* (1859–72) started an important debate and has dominated biological thought ever since.

Patrick Matthew read Thomas Huxley's review of the 1859 edition of the *Origin of Species* and was outraged. He sent a long letter to the *Gardeners' Chronicle* claiming he had introduced the principle of natural selection in a publication in 1831. Darwin answered the letter claiming that no one had ever heard of that publication. Matthew's book, however, had been well reviewed in 1832 in one of the major journals (*Gardeners' Magazine*) by Julius Loudon, the most distinguished arboriculturalist in the country at that time. This was a journal that Darwin subscribed to, the back numbers of which he would have consulted on his return to England in 1836.

Some years later, after the early editions of the *Origin* had been published, Darwin was informed that a Dr W.C. Wells had delivered a paper before the Royal Society in 1813 that involved natural selection. Darwin was overjoyed to hear this because he considered that Matthew could no longer claim to be the first to have introduced natural selection. However, Matthew did not claim to be the first, but had intervened to point out that he had published the concept in 1831.

In the 1872 *Historical Sketch*, Darwin, at long last, acknowledged Lamarck as the first to introduce natural law in place of 'miraculous interposition'. Matthew was also acknowledged as having produced a theory 'precisely similar' to his own. Wells was also acknowledged.

In fact, by claiming that all botanists were aware of natural selection because the vegetables in their gardens demonstrated the power of the breeder in transforming, more quickly than nature, the wild form of vegetables into their domestic form. It was Lamarck who was the first to announce the principle of natural selection. But even Lamarck's remarks were no more than a recapitulation of common knowledge going back at least 100 years. Breeders over the centuries had produced variations of species that could never have survived under natural conditions. Nature can produce new species as well as variations, but breeders had failed to produce new species. There is evidence, from the fossil record, that species show, in their lifetime, little morphological change, sometimes over millions of years.

The process of selection was not just an adage so far as Patrick Matthew was concerned. It was much more – it was a universal law of nature. In 1858 Darwin introduced 'the natural means of selection', but this was reduced to 'natural selection' in the *Origin of Species*. Natural selection had a lukewarm reception and was even opposed by several naturalists, especially Alfred Wallace, who, as we have seen, forced Darwin to substitute 'the survival of the fittest' for natural selection. Darwin accordingly altered the title of Chapter 4. By 1870, however, Wallace had changed his mind and was writing enthusiastically about natural selection. After Darwin died, Wallace assumed the leadership of natural selection.

Natural selection, as it is today, only became firmly established in the 1930s – a hundred years after Patrick Matthew had first published his Appendix to *Naval Timber and Arboriculture* in 1831.

It did not take Marx and Engels long to realise that Victorian biology reflected the imperial interests of Victorian England. In 1872, Engels commented that 'Darwin did not know what a bitter satire he wrote on mankind when he showed that free competition, the struggle for existence, which the economists celebrate as the highest achievement, is the normal state of the animal kingdom.'

Reading through the *Principles of Geology* by Charles Lyell, and in particular the chapter on geographical distribution of species, one has to recognise that there was another naturalist, Decandolle, a friend and colleague of Lamarck, who was aware of the principle of natural selection. In the section on botanical geography Lyell states:

'All the plants of a given country,' says Decandolle in his

186

usual spirited style, 'are at war with one another. The first which establish themselves by chance in a particular spot, tend, by the mere occupancy of space, to exclude other species – the greater choke the smaller, the longest livers replace those which last for a shorter period, the more prolific gradually make themselves masters of the ground, which species multiplying more slowly would otherwise fill'.

That statement can be interpreted as a brief expression of the principle of natural selection, and indicates that Patrick Matthew was influenced by those who preceded him. Because Matthew was daily engaged in selection with his fruit trees he was able to see that there was a principle of selection at work in nature. Here is a passage from Matthew which is quite similar to Decandolle's:

The use of the infinite seedling varieties in the families of plants, even in those in a state of nature, differing in luxuriance of growth and local adaptation, seems to be to give one individual (the strongest best circumstance-suited) superiority over others of its kind around, that it may, by topping and smothering them, procure room for full growth and reproduction.

Darwin knew about Decandolle and mentions him in several of his books. Decandolle was a collaborator with Lamarck who would have agreed what has been quoted. The naturalists of the early 19th century were probably influenced by the naturalists of the 18th century, among whom the dominant character was Buffon. The history of 'the struggle for existence' extends further back than 1859 where many biologists appear to believe it does. But the actual term 'Natural process of selection' appeared in 1831.

187

BIBLIOGRAPHY

Ahouse, J.C., 1998, 'The tragedy of *a priori* Selectionism: Dennett & Gould on Adaptationism', *Biology and Philosophy 13*, 359–391.

Alvarez, L.W., Alvarez, W., Asaro, F. and Michel, H.V., 1980, 'Extraterrestrial Cause for the Cretaceous–Tertiary Extinction'. *Science 208*, 1095–1108.

Atkins, H., 1971, *Hunterian Oration. Ann. Roy. Coll. Surg. Engl.*, 28, 193.

Bak, P. and Snepen, K., 1994, 'Punctuated Equilibrium and criticality in a simple mode of evolution'. *Phys. Rev. 81*, 801–805.

Barker, J.E., 2001, 'Patrick Matthew – Forest Geneticist'. *Forest History Today*, Spring–Fall, 64–65.

Barrett, P.H., Gautrey, P.J., Herbert, S., Kohn, D. and Smith, S., 1987, *Charles Darwin's Note Books*. Cambridge University Press.

Behe, M., 1996, *Darwin's Black Box: The Biochemical Challenge to Evolution*. Free Press.

Blyth, E., 1835–7, *Magazine of Natural History 3*, 40–53. 9, 505–514, 1(NS) 77–85.

Boakes, R., 1984, *From Darwin to Behaviourism*. Cambridge University Press.

Buckle, H.T., 1904, *The History of Civilisation in England*. G. Routledge & Sons.

Calman W.T., 1912, *Patrick Matthew of Gourdiehill, Naturalist*. Hand book. BAAS. Adv. Sci. 451–457.

Chambers, R., 1844, *The Vestiges of the Natural History of Creation*. John Churchill, London.

Clube, V. and Napier, B., 1982, *The Cosmic Serpent*. Faber & Faber, London.

Clube, S.M.V., 1995, 'The Nature of Punctuational Crises and the Splenglerian Model of Civilisation'. *Vistas in Astronomy*. Vol. 39, 673–698.

Coleman, W., 1964, *Georges Cuvier*. Harvard University Press.

Daiches, D., Jones, J. and Jones, P., 1996, *The Scottish Enlightenment*. Saltire Society.

Darlington, C.D., 1961, *Darwin's Place in Nature*. Blackwell, Oxford.

Darwin, C., 1845, *Journal of Researchers*. John Murray, London.

Darwin, C., 1859–1872, *The Origin of Species*. John Murray, London.

Darwin, C., 1868, *Variation in Animals and Plants under Domestication*. John Murray, London.

Darwin, C., 1871, 1874, *The Descent of Man*. John Murray, London.

Darwin, F., 1892, *Life and Letters of Charles Darwin*. John Murray, London.

Dawkins, R., 1988, *The Blind Watchmaker*. Penguin Books.

Dawkins, R., 2003, *A Devil's Chaplain*. Weidenfeld & Nicolson, London.

DeBeer, Gavin, 1961, 'Origins of Darwin's ideas on Evolution & Natural Selection'. *Proc.Roy.Soc.* 155B, 321–338.

Dempster, W.J., 1996, *Evolutionary Concepts in the Nineteenth Century, Natural Selection and Patrick Matthew*. Pentland Press, Durham, England.

Dennett, D.C., 1995, *Darwin's Dangerous Idea*. Allen Lane, The Penguin Press.

Dobzhansky, T., 1970, *Genetics of the Evolutionary Process*. Columbia U.P.

Dover, Gabriel, 2001, *Dear Mr Darwin*. Phoenix.

Dupree, A.H., 1959, *Asa Gray 1810–1888*. Harvard University Press.

Eiseley, L.C., 1959, 'Charles Darwin, Edward Blyth and the Theory of Natural Selection'. *Proc.Amer.Phil.Soc.* 103, no. 1, 94–154.

Eiseley, L., 1961, *Darwin's Century*. Anchor Books, New York.

Eldredge, N. and Gould, S.J., 1972, 'Punctuated Equilibrium: an Alternative to Phyletic Gradualism', in T.J.M. Schopf (ed.), *Models in Paleobiology*, pp. 82–115. Freeman, Cooper & Co., San Francisco.

Eldredge, N., 1986, *Time Frames*. Heinemann, London.

Eldredge, N., 1995, *Reinventing Darwin*. Weidenfeld & Nicolson, London.

Focke, W.D., 1851, *Die Pflanzen – Mischlinge. Ein Beitrag Zur Biologie der Gewashe*. Borntrager, Berlin.

190

Futuyarma, D.J., 1986, *Evolutionary Biology*, Sinauer, Sunderland, MA.

Gayon, J., 1998, *Darwinism's Struggle for Existence*. Cambridge University Press.

Gorman, M.L. and Stone, R.D., 1990, *The Natural History of Moles*. Christopher Helm, London.

Gould, S.J., 1983, 'On Original Ideas', *Natural History 1*, 26–33.

Gould, S.J., 1987, 'The Fraud that Never Was', *New Scientist 113*, 32–36.

Gould, S.J., 1996, *Dinosaur in a Haystack*. Jonathon Cape, London.

Gould, S.J., 2002, *The Structure of Evolutionary Theory*. Belnap Press of Harvard University Press.

Haldane, J.B.S., 1959, 'The Theory of Natural Selection Today', *Nature 183*, 710–713.

Harris, C.L., 1981, *Evolution*. State of New York University Press, Albany.

Harris, H., 1999, *The Birth of the Cell*. Yale University Press.

Hogben, L.T., 1940, *Problems of the Origin of Species in New Systematics*. Ed. Huxley, J. Oxford.

Hull, D.H., 1973, *Darwin and his Critics; the Reception of Evolution by the Scientific Community*. Chicago University Press.

Huxley, J., 1942, *Evolution: The Modern Synthesis*. Allen & Unwin.

Imbrie, J. and Imbrie, K., 1979, *Ice Ages*. Harvard University Press.

Jones, S., 1999, *Almost like a Whale*. Doubleday, London.

Jones, S., 2002, *Y: The Descent of Men*. Little, Brown, London.

Keith, A., 1949, *A New Theory of Human Evolution*. Watts, London.

Kelvin, Lord, 1868, *The Doctrine of Uniformity*. Proc. of Royal Soc., Edinburgh.

King-Hele, D., 1999, *Erasmus Darwin: A Life of Unequalled Achievement*. Giles de la Mare.

Lamarck, J.-B., 1809, *Philosophy of Zoology*. Reprinted Flammarion, G.-F., 1994. Paris.

Lewontin, R., 2000, *It Ain't Necessarily So*. Granta Books, London.

Livesley, B. and Pentelow, G.M., 1978, *The Burning of Hunter's Papers; A New Explanation*. Ann. Roy. Coll. Surg. Engl., 60, 79–84.

Løvetrup, S., 1987, *Darwinism: the Refutation of a Myth*. Croom Helm.

Lyell, C., 1831–1833, *The Principles of Geology*. John Murray.

Matthew, P., 1831, *Naval Timber and Arboriculture.* Adam and Charles Black, Edinburgh; Longman, London.

Matthew, P., 1839, *Emigration Fields.* Adam and Charles Black, Edinburgh; Longman, London.

Maynard-Smith, J., 1982, *Evolution of Sex.* Cambridge University Press.

Maynard-Smith, J. and Szathnary, E., 1999, *The Origin of Life.* Oxford University Press.

Mayr, E., 1964, *Systematics & the origin of species from the viewpoint of a zoologist.* Dover Publications, New York.

Mayr, E., 1982, *The Growth of Biological Thought.* Harvard University Press.

Mayr, E., 2002, *What Evolution Is.* Weidenfeld & Nicolson, London.

McKinney, H.L., 1972, *Wallace and Natural Selection.* Yale University Press, New Haven and London.

Mendel, G., 1866, *Versuche uber Pflanzen-Hybriben.* Brünn.

Miller, G., 2000, *The Mating Mind.* BCA, London.

Miller, J. and Van Loon, B., 1992, *Darwin for Beginners.* Icon Books Ltd., Cambridge.

More, L.T., 1925, *The Dogma of Evolution.* Princeton University Press, New Jersey.

Morris, S.C., 1998, *The Crucible of Creation.* Oxford University Press.

Ospovat, D., 1995, *The Development of Darwin's Theory.* Cambridge University Press. Reprint of 1981 Edition.

Owen, R., Ed., 1861, *Essays & Observations.* London.

Paley, W., 1802, *Natural Theology.* Reprinted Farnborough, Greed, 1970.

Pearson, H., 1930, *Dr Darwin.* T.M. Dent & Sons.

Power, D., 1925, *A Hunterian Oration. Lancet,* 1: 369.

Romanes, G.T., 1893, *Darwin and after Darwin,* 3 vols. Longman, Green & Co., London.

Rose, H. and S., Eds, 2000, *Alas, Poor Darwin.* Jonathan Cape, London.

Rosen, C., 1996, *The Romantic Generation.* HarperCollins.

Ross, I.S., 1995, *The Life of Adam Smith.* Clarendon Press, Oxford.

Ruse, M., 1986, *Taking Darwin Seriously.* Blackwell, Oxford.

Secord, J.A., 2000, *Victorian Sensation.* Chicago University Press.

Smith, L.P., 1943, *Words and Idioms.* Constable, London.

Smolin, L., 1997, *The Life of the Cosmos.* Weidenfeld & Nicholson, London.

Stanley, S.M., 1979, *Macro Evolution: Pattern and Process.* W.H. Freeman & Co., San Francisco.

Sulloway, F.L., 1982, 'Darwin & His Finches: The Evolution of a Legend'. *J. Hist. Biol. 15,* 1–53.

Tudge, C., 2002, *In Mendel's Footnotes.* Jonathan Cape, London.

Vickers, M.J., 1911, 'An Apparently Hitherto Unnoticed "Anticipation" of the Theory of Natural Selection', *Nature 85,* 510–511.

Wallace, A.R., 1881, 1901, *Darwinism. An Exposition of Natural Selection.* Macmillan, London.

Wallace, A.R., 1891, *Natural Selection and Tropical Nature.* Macmillan, London.

Weinstein, A., 1977, 'How Unknown Was Mendel's Paper?' *J. Hist. Biol.,* Vol. 10, No. 2 (Fall 197), pp. 341–346.

Wells, K.D., 1973, 'The Historical Context of Natural Selection. The Case of Patrick Matthew'. *J. Hist. Biol.,* 6, 225–258.

White, M., 1997, *Isaac Newton: The Last Sorcerer.* Fourth Estate, London.

Wightman, W.P.D., 1950, *The Growth of Scientific Ideas.* Oliver & Wood, London.

Wilson, R.A., 1946, *The Miraculous Birth of Language.* The British Publishers Guild.

Wood-Jones, F., 1952, John Hunter as a Geologist. *Ann. Roy. Col. Surg. Engl.,* 11, 219–244.

Zimmer, C., 2002, *Evolution.* William Heinemann.

INDEX

195

196

Livesley, 35
Logan, Pearsall Smith, 32
Lyell, Charles, 1, 2, 6, 69, 75, 76, 85,
  86, 88, 97, 100, 102, 120, 122, 126,
  132, 135, 137, 139, 147, 148, 152,
  154, 156, 161, 162, 165, 166, 171,
  175, 179, 185

Malthus, Thomas R., 77, 100, 101,
  151
mass extinctions, 1, 2, 3, 6, 7, 10, 61,
  64, 72, 73, 75, 76, 79, 84–5, 87–8,
  98, 100, 106, 122, 126, 130, 134,
  146, 147, 148, 150, 151, 154–5, 158,
  161, 162, 165, 171, 174–7, 179, 180,
  181
Mating Mind, 107, 108
Matthew, Patrick, 1, 2, 4, 5, 6, 7–11,
  39–40, 62, 64–5, 68, 70, 72–3, 75,
  80, 83, 86–7, 89, 92, 95–6, 98, 101,
  102, 106, 109–10, 114, 115–16, 118,
  120, 121, 127, 128, 130, 131, 133,
  135, 138, 140–1, 144, 151, 152, 154,
  158, 162, 175, 176, 177, 179, 183,
  185–7,
Maynard Smith, John, 122
Mayr, Ernst, 1, 9, 63, 66, 89, 115, 121
McKinney, H.L., 101, 140, 142
Mendel, Gregor, 2, 72, 74–5, 76–7, 87,
  121, 127
Miller, Jonathan, 103, 104
Montevideo, 169
Morris, Conway, 75
Murray, John, 94, 156
Mutation of species, 132

Natural process of selection, 186
Newton, Isaac, 5, 10, 23, 84, 88, 100,
  155, 169, 179, 183
Noachian Flood, 16

Origin of Language, 4, 34
Origin of Species, 1, 2, 5, 6, 8–9, 16, 30,
  34, 37, 39, 62, 63, 64–5, 67, 69–71,
  73, 75, 77, 78, 83, 88, 93, 94–9, 104,
  108, 109–10, 114–15, 119, 125–30,
  132–9, 143–50, 152, 155, 156, 160–1,
  163–4, 167, 168, 169, 171, 173–5,
  181–2, 185

Ospovat, D., 128, 134, 135, 140, 141,
  147, 149, 150, 151, 152
Owen, Richard, 14, 15, 16, 18, 21, 23,
  25, 27, 28, 31, 64, 71, 74, 99, 120,
  131, 166, 168, 176

Paine, Tom, 18
Paris Basin, 3, 76, 165
Parkinson, James, 21
Pearson, Karl, 2
Philosophy of Zoology, 6, 119, 122, 127,
  144, 152, 153, 157, 158, 159, 162,
  166, 176
Pichot, André, 153
Pictet, 144, 161, 173, 174
polyp, 4, 78
Portugal, 14
Priestley, Joseph, 23
principle of natural selection, 7, 8, 9, 11,
  40, 64, 71, 73, 83, 89, 96, 110, 127,
  132, 133, 139, 184, 185, 186
Providence, 66, 96, 98

Ramsay, Alan, 32
recapitulation, 160, 163
Reversion, 138
reviews, 58
Richmond Park, 20
Robertson, William, 23
Romanes, George, 146
romantic poets, 5
Ross, I.S., 26, 27, 190
Royal Society, 15, 16, 19, 23, 25, 28, 29,
  36, 38, 88, 97, 158, 184
Ruse, M., 77, 78, 79
Rush, Benjamin, 33

Sanskrit, 4
Scottish Enlightenment, 31, 125, 188
secondary sexual characters, 6, 17, 24,
  34, 74, 90, 95, 108, 122, 166, 168,
  169
Secord, J.A., 161
Sedgwick, Adam, 16, 21, 103, 104
Semper, Professor, 138
Smith, Adam, 23, 26, 29, 32, 34, 126
Smolin, Lee, 180
Snell Exhibitionist, 26
Sorbonne, 19, 84

197